The Edwardian Song Book

The Edwardian Song Book

Drawing-Room Ballads, 1900-1914,
from the catalogue of Boosey & Co.

Selected and introduced by
MICHAEL R. TURNER
and ANTONY MIALL

METHUEN

First published in Great Britain 1982 by
Methuen London Ltd
11 New Fetter Lane, London EC4P 4EE

ISBN 0 413 49790 9

Printed in Great Britain by
William Clowes (Beccles) Ltd, Beccles and London

Contents

Introduction

1

Lift the lid of your great-aunt's piano stool and you will be sure to find a few drawing-room ballads. They may be stirring evocations of the mother country like 'Land of Hope and Glory', or excursions into the blossombedecked countryside like 'Glorious Devon', or perhaps exotic expressions of thwarted passion like the 'Kashmiri Song'. Try a few bars on the piano and there may be a start of delighted recognition, for many of the tunes have become embedded in our musical subconscious. Look at the names of the poets and composers: quite a number of songs will be by prestigious figures like Sir Henry Newbolt and Rudyard Kipling, Sir Edward Elgar, Sir Charles Stanford and even Ralph Vaughan Williams. Others, indeed the great bulk of them, will be by writers and musicians almost certainly dead and mostly forgotten. Only their songs remain to tell us how our Edwardian forebears diverted themselves — and how they viewed the world beyond the potted palms.

To perform and hear them now is to conjure up a lost world, of evenings when the family have invited in friends to join together in entertaining themselves, of society soirées when the latest tenor has been lion-hunted (and appropriately reimbursed) to crown the season, and of ballad concerts where the public has turned up in droves to hear old favourites and the latest releases of Messrs Boosey or Messrs Chappell.

Today they are regarded at best as Glorious Rubbish, a splendidly sweeping categorization that embraces fabulous riches and the most abject dross. It is a long time since these ballads were accepted for what they really were, a part of everyday middle-class life. Harold Fraser-Simson, an accomplished composer whom we shall meet later in these pages, remembered exactly how they were seen in the first years of the new century:

> Ballads sold in those days. No-one with any pretensions to a voice, and many people who had not even this, would dream of going out to dinner without his, or her music. The music was left outside with the coats and fetched shyly, after the correct amount of hanging about.

There were good ballads, bad ballads and a great ocean of the mediocre. Highbrow critics sneered at what they called 'shop ballads', but the public blithely went on buying them by the million. Celebrated composers later affected to despise them, but at the time wrote them for love — and for money. Leading singers included them in their repertoires in great quantity; even a fabulous international diva like Luisa Tetrazzini was expected to render them as a matter of course. When she failed to include 'Home, Sweet Home' in her first concert in London in 1907, *The Graphic* complained pettishly: 'If she imagines she can retain her hold upon the affections of the British public without it, it is to be feared that she is doomed to disappointment. . . . [her] daring will lead to disastrous results.'

1

As for the great British singers of the day like the magisterial Dame Clara Butt, no concert was complete without a generous ration of cosy sublimity in ballad form. And not only were these songs woven into daily life, they were the manifestation of an immense support industry of lyricists, composers, publishers, singers, accompanists and concert-promoters.

2

In our two previous collections, *The Parlour Song Book* and *Just a Song at Twilight*, we presented representative gems from the rich mine of Victorian song, up to the year 1900. In this volume we venture into the next significant period of 1900-14, before the Great War altered British society irreversibly and with it the manner and matter of its amusements. Although these years do not correspond exactly with the those of Edward VII's accession and death, we have applied the title 'Edwardian' to them, as have others, not simply for convenience or to justify the title of our anthology, but because the cushioned yet oddly sour beginning of the reign of George V was much closer in spirit to the decade that preceded it than to the time of conflict and upheaval that followed.

It is recognized by scholars nowadays that an understanding of social attitudes and modes of life is as crucial to the grasp of a period as is that of major historical events. The interests of the people, as seen through their popular art, are essential to that understanding. No longer do we confine the term 'folk-art' to the anonymous, orally transmitted creations of workers in the country and town, but widen it to include broadsheet ballads, music-hall songs, penny dreadfuls and other matter written, often by identifiable individuals, and published to make money. For some reason, that increasing liberalism has not gone so far as to embrace drawing-room music, and yet the 'shop ballad' was as integral to the life of the suburban parlour, the country house and the fashionable salon as were music-hall ditties to that of the pubs and homes of working-class Britain. It only needs a small step: we nominate drawing-room ballads as an essential part of the folk-art of the middle classes.

3

Naturally, the advent of a new century and a new monarch did not bring overnight change to the subject-matter of ballads; but there were certainly marked differences, both general and specific, between the songs of the 1890s and those of the 1900s. That supremely professional and prolific lyricist Fred E. Weatherly, who will accompany us through this book, put it succinctly: 'No more songs,' he said, 'of beggar children going to heaven on triplets.' On their way out were dying babies (although they were too good a topic ever to vanish completely), consumptive mothers, old armchairs, negligent signalmen, sinking ships, disasters natural and man-made, and the whole world of the damp handkerchief. In came the imperial theme of Britain, with her noble mission to set the world a good example; in came the English countryside, complete with a cast of farmers, apple-cheeked maidens, gypsies and tinkers; in came the sturdy common soldierman who no longer died with a hoarse whisper of 'Mother!' on his lips but marched into battle whether the Gatling was jammed or not; in came Elizabethan sea-dogs who, when they were not a-dancin' heel-an'-toe, had dire intentions on the King of Spain's beard; and in came a new style of love-making. This was either pretty, misty and winsome, characterized by coy whisperings in the twilight — spooning — or else it was passionate and primitive, usually taking place not far from the Shalimar gardens. There was still a fair sprinkling of mossy graves about the ballad countryside, although the genteel taste for easeful death was soon to come to an abrupt end when faced by the realities of the battlefields of Flanders.

One of the most typically Edwardian innovations, to our eyes, was the flood of ballads about the non-commissioned soldier and sailor: from 'The Company Sergeant-Major', by way of 'A Sergeant of the Line' and 'Corporal Mike' down to 'Private Tommy Atkins', and, on the bounding main, 'Ben the Bo'sun', 'The Red Marine', 'Jack Tar' and their shipmates. Kipling had a lot to do with their introduction, but they drew upon many elements of the time, imperialist braggadocio, the discovery of the quaint common man, music-hall and the delight in funny dialects.

Some themes continued from the nineteenth century with very little change: Irish songs, real and imitation, yearnings for home, and the frontiers of Araby expanded to embrace further exotic tracts of Asia, from India to Korea, down the continent of Africa, across the Americas and up into Lapland, with titles as diverse as a 'Cossack Cradle Song', 'A Maori Canoe' and 'Nada: a Zulu Warrior's Love Song'.

Today we are inclined to pay more attention to the music and to close the ear to the outdated texts, but for a proper understanding of what the ballad meant to its Edwardian audience it is essential to listen to what is being sung. One would expect the lyricists to emphasize the importance of their verse, and they did so *ad nauseam* — Fred E. Weatherly was almost obsessive on the subject — but so did many of the singers. Lillian Nordica wrote in 1907 'the sentiment of a ballad is of almost more importance than the music', the Victorian Antoinette Sterling said that she could not render a song properly unless she truly believed in the words, and Dame Clara Butt echoed that sentiment. That formidable lady, the apotheosis of the genteel, had a magnificent self-confidence: 'I have sung many songs during my career, and I do not think I have sung any bad ones.' What a long way this is from the directness of the advice her contemporary, Dame Nellie Melba, gave to Dame Clara before she embarked on an Australian tour: 'Sing 'em muck,' she said. 'It's all they understand.'

But that splendid admonition is unique in the annals of drawing-room song. The whole subject was generally treated with enormous solemnity by all involved, perhaps because even then critics were snapping round the heels of the ballad industry, pointing out the vapidity of much of its enormous output. The more popular song-writers were indignant at this denigration of their craft, pointing out that serious composers did not disdain this art-form and received plaudits whilst the efforts of the best-selling song-smiths were sneered at as 'shop ballads': a familiar and long-lived complaint heard even in the 1980s when block-buster novelists are stung to protest at the apparent critical disdain for their sterling work.

But what of those 'better' composers? Even the public accolade of knighthood, conferred on those whose music was critically and socially respectable, did not cause them to draw away the skirts of their frock coats from the ballad: Sir Edward Elgar, Sir Hubert Parry, Sir Frederic Cowen, Sir Charles Stanford and Sir Arthur Sullivan, as well as the untitled non-popular composers like Ralph Vaughan Williams and Percy Grainger, all participated in the boom. Sir Frederic Cowen explained in the 1920s, rather shamefacedly, for by then the reputation of drawing-room music was hastening to its nadir, 'At that period, serious music yielded very little money, and we musicians had to live', and in self-justification he pointed out that 'some seventy or eighty of my songs were on serious lines'. The tendency for ballads to be put together with greater musical sophistication than before, exemplified by the emergence of the 'art ballad', was already obvious by the end of the nineteenth century but the polarization of popular and serious, so characteristic of the later years of the next century, had hardly begun. The programmes of many, many ballad concerts show how catholic was contemporary taste, for serious works were performed cheek by jowl with pot-boilers.

4

Ballad singing, that most popular of all Victorian indoor sports, and the phenomenally wide acceptance of the piano above all other musical instruments, together laid the foundations of a movement in the mid-nineteenth century that lasted well into the twentieth. The popularity of parlour song was not rooted only in sentimentality: the form was far more vigorous and developed than present-day critics admit. Whilst the middle classes sang Stephen Adams in their drawing-rooms they also attended concerts of Schubert and Schumann at the Queen's Hall and, as we have seen, even those concerts were apt to mix light and serious material. So the public were happy to see their domestic musical fare reflect the characteristics of more 'respectable' compositions.

Tastes widened. The amateur wanted greater sophistication. The three-decker ballad remained in favour with Edwardian musicians and many examples appear in this collection. Harmonies, however, had become more daring and modulation was *de rigeur*, even if, as in Amy Woodforde-Finden's style, it was merely illusory.

More light comic songs were composed. Short, lyrical pieces achieved an enormous vogue. The most significant musical product for the amateur in the early twentieth century, however, was the song cycle. This essentially German form, dating back some eighty years or so and dignified in text books with its indigenous name, *Liederkreis*, was taken up by Edwardian composer and amateur musician alike with almost Victorian ardour. When Liza Lehmann's cycle *The Daisy Chain* first appeared it became the centre-piece of 'Daisy Chain Tours', 'Daisy Chain At-Homes' and 'Daisy Chain Concerts'. Her more famous cycle *In a Persian Garden* of the nineties undoubtedly received more performances than any other. The Americans helped to spread the fashion, as Miss Lehmann herself observed: 'I still regard America as the *Persian Garden's* fairy godmother, to the kindness of whose reception I owe everything.' The respectable Landon Ronald, son of that great Victorian note-spinner Henry Russell, whose 'A Life on the Ocean Wave' no doubt helped with his son's expensive musical education, jumped nimbly on to the band-wagon with his *A Cycle of Life* which included the immensely popular 'Down in the Forest Something Stirred'. The composer and arranger H. Lane Wilson scored an enormous success with his cycle *Flora's Holiday*, and Amy Woodforde-Finden, steeped in oriental echoes, produced *Four Indian Love Lyrics*, *On Jhelum River*, *A Lover in Damascus*, *Five Little Japanese Songs* and many other collections. The song cycle was an inescapable fact of Edwardian drawing-room life.

Towards the end of the period there was a noticeable reaction against shorter songs and cycles in favour of the tried and trusted ballad. The old three-decker was once again in the ascendant in the hand of composers like Wilfrid Sanderson. Even after the Great War, when amateur music was in full decline, the ballad form subsisted and was incorporated into the popular dance songs of the 'twenties and 'thirties. Indeed, it has never really gone away as the present-day 'chart-watcher' knows.

Many Edwardian ballads look remarkably simple. They were, and remain, something of a challenge for even the most accomplished performer, although beginners can have an immense amount of enjoyment in attempting them and reasonably able amateurs can delight audiences as well as themselves. Madame Antoinette Sterling, one of the foremost exponents of the ballad before and during our period, gave solemn warning:

> People think ballads are easy to sing. As a matter of fact they are the most difficult of all music to render with true effect. The ballad is simple in words, melody and accompaniment. There is nothing to help out the singer. It depends entirely on the power of expression, the intensity and variety of feeling. It is a question of art, interpretation and personality combined.

On reading that one imagines the amateur was supposed to creep away into a corner.

Nonetheless, when the elements identified by Madame Sterling are employed, the results can be magical. Despite the evidence of early recordings, it is still difficult to recapture the full effect of a rendering of eighty years ago, but there is no reason to doubt the truth of this critical judgment: 'To hear Madame Butt sing is to learn in a moment what a god-like gift the power of song is! . . . the rendition of the simplest ballad by her at once holds her hearers spellbound by the artistic wealth with which she illuminates it.' So, if such great skill seems to be required, what hope is there for the amateur of the late twentieth century? We can take heart from the indisputable success of innumerable amateurs all those years ago; they were not daunted by the problems that the Sterlings and the Butts needed all their resources to overcome. We simply have to pay attention to how the Edwardians themselves approached their songs.

In her book *Love's Shadow* Ada Leverson gives us a fascinating glimpse into an Edwardian aristocrat's music-room: 'Lord Selsey had one room for music. There was a little platform at the end of it and no curtains or draperies to obscure or stifle sound.' Miss Leverson goes on to describe every detail of the decor, and finally mentions the fact that the room contained small Empire sofas 'in which no more than two persons could be seated'. This, she points out triumphantly, ensured that the audiences often enjoyed themselves as much as the performers — adding gloomily, 'which is rare'.

There can be no doubt that musical evenings at the turn of the century could be very dull. The Edwardians, like the Victorians before them, set great store by enthusiasm, and a well-meaning end was often held to justify excruciating means. However, the new songs becoming available offered much more scope to the singer and, one hopes, more enjoyment to the audience. The flow of ballads which had been a trickle on the 1860s was by 1900 an irresistible tide which encouraged really first-class classically-trained composers to take it at the flood, and they brought some very fine songs to the drawing-room. Standards generally improved as the public responded to a greater degree of sophistication, and many of the compositions in this collection are as musically satisfying as any in the English language.

With the growth of the recording industry — which at this period catered mostly for the moneyed middle classes — artistes of the first rank added ballads to their classical recording repertoire, partly, of course, because they sold but also, as anyone who has heard discs of the time by Chaliapin, McCormack or Peter Dawson will know, because they enjoyed singing them.

Here, then, lie the clues to the appropriate rendition of Edwardian songs. First, they are to be enjoyed. Secondly, the performers should beware of showy self-indulgence — unless there are Empire sofas about the place. And thirdly, the songs should be approached as intelligently as possible. Composers of ballads at the beginning of the century were scrupulous in indicating tempo, dynamics and phrasing. This was the inevitable result of the greater number of professionals entering the field. The characterized performances of the nineteenth century with their strong operatic overtones tended to fall from favour as a new suavity of approach became fashionable.

Performers of these songs today will find, as Edwardian singers did, that all they need to know is on the page. Follow the markings faithfully and the pieces will spring to life as freshly as they did for our grandparents.

5

At first it may seem strange to confine this selection of songs to the catalogue of a single publisher, for there were many houses, among them the important firm of Chappell, pouring out hundreds of songs annually to feed an avid public. But there is something special about the list issued by Boosey & Co.; the company was the undisputed leader in the field and its business was dependent upon a unique integration of its ballad concerts and sheet-music publishing. Its catalogue, therefore, had a remarkable cohesion and richness and a selection from it encapsulates the Edwardian taste. Even in the 1980s when probably no composer or lyricist represented in these pages remains alive, copyright problems loom large for the anthologizer of ballads — for instance, it has sadly not been possible to include a major item, 'The Road to Mandalay' by Rudyard Kipling and Oley Speaks, though it is now published by Boosey & Hawkes — and it is only with the willing co-operation of that firm that the present volume has been made feasible.

The house of Boosey began as a lending library in the City of London, founded by John Boosey sometime between 1765 and 1770; Samuel Taylor Coleridge was one of his customers. John's son Thomas expanded the business, especially in the direction of scientific and educational books which necessitated visits to the Continent. It was on these trips that his musical interests developed, and he started to import foreign sheet music. By 1816 this sideline had grown so much that he transferred the music business, by then located in Holles Street near Oxford Circus (the firm Boosey & Hawkes still has a shop and offices very close by) to his son Thomas, and sold the circulating library a few years later. Illustrious names now appeared in the catalogue, among them Beethoven, Hummel, Rossini, Donizetti, Bellini and Verdi, and Thomas's son John launched a number of cheap editions of the classics. Opera and operetta were a particular speciality, and in mid-century, branching out again, the firm began to manufacture wind and brass instruments, an activity that has since been as important a part of Boosey's business as publishing.

The nineteenth-century Booseys seem to have been a singularly bene-volent breed. It is said of John, instigator of the firm's ballad concerts and with them the great list of ballads, that he induced much affection in com-posers and artistes; his premier lyricist Fred E. Weatherly dedicated a song to him: 'Uncle John'. The singer Plunket Greene wrote of John Boosey's nephew Arthur that he had 'been treated with the utmost kindness' by him and was never pressed by him to do anything he didn't care about. Another nephew, William, went on to manage the rival house of Chappell but his relationship with the family appears to have remained comfortable, and his warm-hearted if self-satisfied autobiography *Fifty Years of Music* provides a lively glimpse of the crowded life of the ballad publisher and concert promoter. William Boosey contributed enormously to the health of the music-publishing industry, and he had a lot to be satisfied about.

After the Great War Boosey & Co. diversified again, into educational music and the publication of serious contemporary works. It was in vigorous competition on the musical instrument side as well as in publishing military and brass-band material with the firm of Hawkes & Son, and in 1930 Leslie Boosey proposed amalgamation to Ralph Hawkes. The merger was accom-plished and the house of Boosey & Hawkes developed further as a major international publisher and manufacturer with subsidiary companies in the USA, Canada and Australia.

The great majority if not all of the ballads in this volume were first introduced to the public at ballad concerts. This form of entertainment was as crucial to the success of the music publisher as the practice of 'song-plugging' on the radio and television was to be later in the century; at one time there were no less than four series of ballad concerts running concur-rently in London, promoted by the firms of Boosey, Chappell, Enoch and Cramer.

The publisher Arthur Chappell started it all in January 1859 when he launched in St James's Hall a series of Monday chamber concerts, augmented in 1865 by another series on Saturdays. These were the Saturday and Monday 'Pops', which became such a feature of the middle-class musical scene for nearly fifty years and celebrated in the works of many writers from W.S. Gilbert (it was Archibald Grosvenor in *Patience* who, transformed from a fleshly poet to an 'every-day young man', declared he was the type 'Who thinks suburban 'hops'/More fun than Monday Pops') to Robert Browning who wrote a sonnet on Chappell and the Pops. The formula was a mixture of ballads and instrumental pieces, later including classical chamber music. Not to be outdone, John Boosey started his series of concerts in 1867, concen-trating on ballads only, at the St James's Hall, later alternating with Chappell on Saturdays at the newly built Queen's Hall, later again ambitiously hiring the Albert Hall. The performers at these London ballad concerts included pretty well all the great names in English singing: Madame Antoinette Sterling, who did not miss a single Boosey concert for more than twenty years, Sims Reeves, Edward Lloyd, Sir Charles Santley, Ben Davies, Madame Patey, Madame Sainton-Dolby, Clara Novello, Liza Lehmann and the formid-able Dame Clara Butt, Boosey's ultimate weapon in the rivalry with Chap-pell, helping to establish a considerable lead over his competitor by launch-ing such songs as 'Abide with Me' and 'Land of Hope and Glory'. John McCormack was one of the great singers to make his name at Boosey's concerts, first appearing in 1907. Chappell escalated its weaponry by intro-ducing light orchestras and recitations by famous stage stars, on one occa-sion reducing all present to tears when William Boosey, then managing the

Chappell concerts, during a rendering by Lady Bancroft of Tennyson's 'I'll be Queen of the May, Mother' at the crucial moment 'turned the organ on'.

Sir Frederic Cowen, the eminently respectable and serious composer of symphonic, operatic and choral music, was dogged in later life by his celebrity as the perpetrator in the 1870s of 'The Better Land', one of the most successful ballads ever written. In his autobiography he quoted verses in ballad style by the lyricist Robert Francillon. 'Fred' in the refrain is, of course, Cowen himself.

> When I survey the glorious scene
>   A Ballad Concert shows —
> The singers dressed in pink or green,
>   The audience all in rows —
> To write a song I burn to try,
>   A song — oh, pride to tell!
> For Boosey's customers to buy,
>   And Boosey's self to sell.
>
> And now I've got to do the trick
>   Without a fear at all,
> That Fred won't find a tune to tick-
>   Le up the Albert Hall.
>
> Yes, I have got to write a song;
>   At least I've promised to.
> They tell me it must not be long,
>   Or else it will not do.
> In just two stanzas there must be
>   A little story jammed,
> Or else 'twill never sell, you see
>   And surely will be d--d.
>
> And oh, a short refrain must come
>   With sentimental tears,
> For Fred to make a tune to hum
>   And tickle people's ears.

There are several more stanzas to this wickedly accurate summing-up of the 'shop ballad', one of which describes the urgent need 'To please the man that finds the sticks/that make the pot to boil' — the publisher Boosey.

As Francillon points out, the major objective for the publisher-promoter at ballad concerts was to stimulate sales of sheet music. Favoured pieces were repeated over and over again, and these were only entrusted to star singers; it was very difficult for a new vocalist to get established, for the ballads believed to have potential were not available, and success could only come with the right song in the space of just three or four minutes.

The form of the concerts solidified into a ritual. When anything out of the ordinary was introduced either in the form of unusual material or an unsuitable singer such as a light-opera artiste, the established prima donnas were scandalized, and said so in no uncertain terms. To one such protester, William Boosey riposted that he was sorry for the distress, but that at all events the interloper sang in tune.

The high-water mark for Boosey's ballads was in 1919 when more than two million copies were sold. But the gramophone and then the radio were to effect a profound change in how people entertained themselves at home; the gathering was increasingly round the new boxes of electro-mechanical wonders rather than round the piano. Ballad concerts survived until 1936, a surprisingly late date.

The business aspects of the ballad are fascinating. Until John Boosey, with a remarkable gesture of magnanimity to his composers and to the evident chagrin of his competitors, introduced the royalty system to Britain, song-writers were paid a single fee for each piece; the history of popular song in the Victorian period is crammed with stories of indigent composers 'cheated' of their brain-children for a few pounds or dollars.

The royalty system was extended for many years to leading singers as a means of encouraging them to popularize the latest vocal gems. Madame Antoinette Sterling, for example, augmented her income for many years from such successes of 'hers' as 'The Lost Chord' and 'Love's Old Sweet Song'. The practice lapsed for a while until Dame Clara Butt achieved sufficient power over publishers to reintroduce it. The ballad was at the forefront, too, of the struggle by musicians and their publishers to establish effective copyright legislation. Pirates waxed fat on illegal reprints of songs, and it was only by means of a music publishers' strike in 1905 and an outcry organized by the Musical Defence League that a private bill, the Copyright Act of 1906, was forced through Parliament. At last in 1911 a long overdue new bill replaced previous legislation, making it a criminal offence to pirate music (but still only a civil offence to pirate books!). Sadly, this act was flawed, and even today and several acts later there remain major problems over the mechanical copying of artists' work.

6

Much of the popular concept of the Edwardian period is reflected in these songs: a sublime pride in the mother country, an arrogance only slightly humbled by the Boer War, a love of the countryside, an unabashed nostalgia for the past glories, a steaming romanticism, above all the appearance of a national self-confidence that was to be so abruptly shattered in the mud of Northern France and never regained. We know now that the self-confidence was already a sham, that the glitter and material comfort of Edwardian high society masked poverty, injustice and industrial unrest, and that the scarlet rose of British imperialism was already overblown and cankered.

Yet, for all the bombast and fustian, the false serenity and the insistent whiff of decay, there was something great about the period, in its literature, music and painting, in the dedication of its public servants at home and abroad, in the awakening of social conscience. True, it was red-faced, but it was also red-blooded. Edward VII was himself a potent symbol of the new century: a middle-aged but supremely vigorous and charming prince succeeding a tight-lipped reclusive queen, a known libertine and bon viveur following the personification of rectitude and piety. The Edwardian age — for it was an age, if only a few years long — released pent-up public emotions and engaged in a relieving, self-indulgent spree.

Introduction

It is common to see in Edwardian Britain the apotheosis of the imperial creed. There was, in fact, strongly expressed distaste in many quarters for the political doctrine of Empire and the accompanying jingoism. It was not only the socialists who rejected what they saw as a mixture of barbaric conquest, commercial self-interest and romantic nonsense; the Liberal Party was deeply and noisily split on the matter.

It was a time of great social upheaval: these years saw the suffragette movement releasing a wave of fury, the rise of the Labour Party and the violent industrial strife of 1910-11 leading to what some considered the brink of civil war in 1914. The first truly popular newspapers burgeoned mightily, the cinema arrived, the automobile began to revolutionize transport, man achieved powered flight and ragtime swept away the lancers and quadrilles. The pace was hectic, but the maelstrom was in startling contrast to another characteristic of the time. For the ruling class it was still the high summer of leisure and security. Edwardian comfort and wealth, the products of international trade and imperial expansion, were enjoyed by comparatively few; for many it was a period of creeping depression. In real terms wages actually fell in the first fourteen years of the century, manufacturing output stagnated and the British class structure, riven by ever-increasing material differences, hardened into even greater rigidity. For most of the working class imperialism had nothing solid to offer.

All this doubt and ferment was for the real world; none of it was ever reflected in the texts of ballads. A reading of their verses brings a gradual, awful realization that they represent a blending of the myths that insulated the middle classes from the actuality of life; to a large extent they perpetuated the comfortable Victorian blandness and sustained the rosy glow produced by material riches. Despite all the evidence of the Boer War, the agricultural depression and the fickleness of human affections it was necessary to see soldiers as heroic and chivalrous, the countryside as jolly, quaint and idyllic and love as constant and selfless. If religion had been the opium of the masses, drawing-room ballads were the opium of the middle classes.

Why then do they still hold such attractions? Nostalgia certainly plays a large part, even if we know that the *ante-bellum* world of the 1900s that they portray was a never-never-land — and it was an Edwardian who coined that phrase. But once the songs are actually performed before an audience all the historical and sociological significances give place to enjoyment: the best of the ballads, despite all the weaknesses of the genre, still retain much of their power to charm. They were never designed to stimulate any profound intellectual response. In a musical and literary sense most of them may be meretricious. Written for enjoyment, they gave enormous pleasure in their time and for all the denigration thrown at them they have continued to do so. They were directed at the emotions.

So open this book to a ballad of your choice, open the piano lid, open your mouth — and your mind — and sing!

MICHAEL R. TURNER
ANTONY MIALL
May 1982

1

Land of Hope and Glory

or, Songs of Empire

ENGLAND, MY ENGLAND

Words by
William Ernest Henley

Music by
Frances Allitsen

What have I done for you, Eng-land, my Eng-land?

What is there I would not do, Eng-land, my own?

With your glor-ious eyes aus-tere, As the Lord__ were walk-ing near,

England, My England

Whisp'ring ter-ri-ble things and dear__ As the Song____ on your bu-gles blown,

Eng - land, Eng - land, Round the world__ on your bu - gles

blown!

Where shall the watch-ful Sun, Eng - land, my Eng - land,

Match the mas - ter - work you've done, Eng - land, my own?

13

Land of Hope and Glory

When shall he re-joice a-gen Such a breed of might-y men

As come for-ward, one to ten, To the Song on your bu-gles

blown, Eng-land, Eng-land, Down the

years on your bu-gles blown?

Ev-er the faith en-dures, Eng-land, my Eng-land:

14

England, My England

ENGLAND, MY ENGLAND

1. What have I done for you,
   England, my England?
   What is there I would not do,
   England, my own?
   With your glorious eyes austere,
   As the Lord were walking near,
   Whisp'ring terrible things and dear
   As the Song on your bugles blown,
   England, England,
   Round the world on your bugles blown!

2. Where shall the watchful Sun,
   England, my England,
   Match the masterwork you've done,
   England, my own?
   When shall he rejoice agen
   Such a breed of mighty men
   As come forward, one to ten,
   To the Song on your bugles blown,
   England, England,
   Down the years on your bugles blown?

3. Ever the faith endures,
   England, my England:
   'Take and break us: we are yours,
   England, my own!
   Life is good, and joy runs high
   Between English earth and sky;
   Death is death; but we shall die
   To the Song on your bugles blown,
   England, England,
   To the stars on your bugles blown!'

4. They call you proud and hard,
   England, my England:
   You with worlds to watch and ward,
   England, my own!
   You whose mailed hand keeps the keys
   Of such teeming destinies
   You could know nor dread nor ease
   Were the Song on your bugles blown,
   England, England,
   Round the Pit on your bugles blown!

5. Mother of Ships whose might,
   England, my England,
   Is the fierce old Sea's delight,
   England, my own,
   Chosen daughter of the Lord,
   Spouse-in-Chief of the ancient sword,
   There's the menace of the Word
   In the Song on your bugles blown,
   England, England,
   Out of heaven on your bugles blown!

The ballad version of 'England, My England' was shortened from the poem Henley originally entitled 'Pro Rege Nostro' from the sequence 'For England's Sake'. The original poem includes two more stanzas which characterize an Amazonian England as proud and hard, whose mailed hand keeps the keys to the teeming destinies of sundry worlds and who is coterminously Mother of Ships, chosen daughter of the Lord and Spouse-in-Chief of the ancient Sword. The Sword's other wives are not listed. The word 'agen' in the second stanza is nothing more mysterious than an archaic form of 'again'; it was used by Milton and no doubt was introduced here to provide a note of artistic verisimilitude. This setting of the poem was far from being the only one: Boosey itself published another by Martin Shaw in 1913.

It is ironic that England's most pugnaciously patriotic bard had god-like good looks but was in fact a cripple from the age of twelve and a prey to ill-health all his life. William Ernest Henley (1849-1903) was a successful journalist, critic and playwright; most of his poetry dates from the last fifteen years of his life. His finest work was the powerful and deeply moving volume *In Hospital*, the product of treatment under Lister in Edinburgh

Infirmary, published in the year of the poet's death. A clue to Henley's place in his time may be found in his remarkable anthology of verse for boys *Lyra Heroica*, published originally in 1891 but enjoying its greatest sales in school editions in the Edwardian period. It is a rumbustious collection but surprisingly advanced in its choice of modern writers. It is also significant that the anthologist concluded the book with three of his own most flamboyantly chauvinistic pieces.

Frances Allitsen (1849-1912) was a Miss Bumpus, so it was not surprising, commented William Boosey, mindful of the famous London bookshop, that she had a fine sense of literature. She was a singer who turned her hand to composition: 'I had no technical knowledge, and found it difficult to put my songs on paper.' She showed her early attempts to the head of the Guildhall School of Music; he was so impressed that he offered her a free scholarship in the theory of music. That she learned rapidly is indicated by the fact that her celebrated ballad 'Song of Thanksgiving' was first considered by her publishers to be too difficult for the pianist. Her most famous setting was of Charles Mackay's 'There's a Land, a Dear Land', which lay neglected on a shelf at her publishers until Queen Victoria's Jubilee, when the headmistress of a ladies' school exploited the occasion with an extra verse relating to the Queen. The augmented song was an instant success, and when Dame Clara Butt adopted it Allitsen's career as a composer was secure. She employed her talents particularly in two types of ballad, patriotic and religious, and so forthright were those of the former that the public often believed her to be a man. Once at dinner another guest whom she had not previously met confided in her that he knew the composer: 'Old Frank Allitsen. . . A jolly old chap he is too; we often have a game of billiards together.'

Allitsen's Elgarian setting of 'England, My England' predates 'Land of Hope and Glory' by two years, but is very much in the same musical vein. The unmistakeable martial strains are accentuated with bugle calls and nationalist fervour pervades each bar. A spirited rendering of this ballad could surely still persuade impressionable young men to take the Queen's shilling. This fine setting is harmonically adventurous and rhythmically extremely stirring.

LAND OF HOPE AND GLORY

Words by
Arthur C. Benson

Music by
Edward Elgar

Dear Land of Hope, thy hope is crowned, God make thee might - ier yet! On Sov - 'ran brows, be - loved, re - nowned,— Once more thy crown is set. Thine e - qual laws, by — Free-dom gained, Have ruled thee well and long;— By

Land of Hope and Glory

Free-dom gained, by Truth main-tained, Thine Em - pire shall be strong.

Land of Hope and Glo - ry, Mo-ther of the Free,

How shall we ex - tol thee, who are born of thee?

Wi - der still and wi - der shall thy bounds be set;

God, who made thee might - y, make thee might - ier yet;

19

Land of Hope and Glory

God, who made_ thee might - y, make thee might - ier yet.

CHORUS

Land of Hope_ and Glo - ry, Mo-ther of _ the Free,

How shall we ex - tol thee,_____ who are born_ of thee? Wi - der still_ and

wi - der shall thy bounds be .set; God, who made_ thee might - y,

make thee might - ier yet; God, who made_ thee might - y,

20

Land of Hope and Glory

make thee might - ier yet.

Thy fame is an - cient as the days, As O - cean large and wide; _____ A

pride that dares, and heeds not praise _ A stern and si - lent pride;

Not that false joy _ that _ dreams con-tent With what our sires have won; _ The

blood a he - ro sire hath spent Still nerves _ a he - ro son.

Land of Hope and Glory

Molto maestoso

Land of Hope and Glo - ry, Mo-ther of __ the Free,

How shall we ex - tol thee, __ who are born __ of thee?

cresc.

Wi - der still __ and wi - der shall thy bounds be set;

God, who made __ thee might - y, make thee might - ier yet;

allargando

God, who made __ thee might - y, make thee might - ier yet.

Land of Hope and Glory

LAND OF HOPE AND GLORY

1. Dear Land of Hope, thy hope is crowned,
   God make thee mightier yet!
   On Sov'ran brows, beloved, renowned,
   Once more thy crown is set.
   Thine equal laws, by Freedom gained,
   Have ruled thee well and long;
   By Freedom gained, by Truth maintained,
   Thine Empire shall be strong.

   Land of Hope and Glory,
   Mother of the Free,
   How shall we extol thee,
   Who are born of thee?
   Wider still and wider shall thy bounds be set;
   God, who made thee mighty, make thee mightier yet;
   God, who made thee mighty, make thee mightier yet.

2. Thy fame is ancient as the days,
   As Ocean large and wide;
   A pride that dares, and heeds not praise,
   A stern and silent pride;
   Not that false joy that dreams content
   With what our sires have won;
   The blood a hero sire hath spent
   Still nerves a hero son.

   Land of Hope and Glory, *etc.*

'I've got a tune', wrote Elgar to Miss Dora Penny, the 'Dorabella' of the *Enigma Variations*, 'that will knock 'em — knock 'em flat.' He conceived it whilst at work on the *Cockaigne* overture and used it some months later as the trio in the first of the two *Pomp and Circumstance* marches which were rapturously received at their first performance in London in 1901. 'You have composed a tune which will go round the world', was the reputed comment of King Edward VII who suggested that it should be sung. Elgar thereupon adapted the melody for words specially written by A.C. Benson for the *Coronation Ode* which was to have been given at Covent Garden in Coronation week. In fact, the gala never took place because of the King's appendicitis, and the first performance was in Sheffield a few months later, in October 1902, when it was rendered with great splendour by Dame Clara Butt. The ballad version printed here was arranged for piano and Benson's words were considerably revised for it. The composer also made another setting for piano and cello as a 'Duet for two nice people by another (nice) Person, op x'. The King was right about the melody; it is now the most popular of popular classics and is still roared out each year by the predominantly youthful audience at the final evening of the BBC Promenade Concerts. An attempt in 1967 to drop the tradition was met by a huge storm of protest.

Later in his life Elgar remarked wistfully, 'A tune like that comes once in a lifetime.' Although he was a melodious composer he is not, perhaps, remembered for his tunes in the same way that some other composers are. It is not surprising that this one outstanding melody should have been seized upon by the public and have established Elgar as a nationalist composer: it has stood the test of time because it is an irresistible 'sing'.

'Land of Hope and Glory', although never conceived as such, was Elgar's only really popular ballad. Although he did say rather pompously that 'Art has nothing to do with the frivolous, nor have I', Elgar had a relish for the tuneful composers of his youth, Suppé and Meyerbeer among them, and wrote some charming light music. His taste was for the full-blooded and not for what he called anaemic music, and although he wrote a number of fine songs such as *Sea Pictures*, his vocal music was more suited to the concert platform and the cathedral than the drawing-room. After the comparative failure of the first performance of *The Dream of Gerontius* friends encouraged him to try his hand at popular ballads, but the results were derivative and unimpressive.

Sir Edward William Elgar (1857-1934) was born at Broadheath in Worcestershire. His father kept a music shop in which his talented son served from time to time, together with the rest of his numerous family. Young Elgar took up the violin and studied for a while in London, but returned to the country to help his father and work as a general musical hack, teaching, playing in local performances, composing lancers, quadrilles and polkas to order and at one time acting as bandmaster of an attendants' orchestra at a lunatic asylum. He married an artistic and cultivated admirer some eleven years older than he was, and with her devoted help dedicated himself to serious composition. Success was a long time coming, but when it did arrive with the première of the *Enigma Variations* in 1899 it was instantaneous. The great works now tumbled one upon the other: *Gerontius* in 1900, *Cockaigne* and the first two *Pomp and Circumstance* marches in 1901 and then the honour of the *Coronation Ode* the following year. In 1904 a three-day Elgar Festival at Covent Garden and a knighthood confirmed his celebrity in no uncertain manner. From then on he became a national monument, and his sensitive, somewhat withdrawn nature became masked by a populist imperial image. *The Sketch* thought he might pass 'for an Army officer in mufti' rather than a musician. Elgar's passionate love for the Malvern Hills and the countryside of Worcestershire was more of a clue to his restless and complex character.

Arthur Christopher Benson (1862-1925) who wrote the words for this immortal song is now a dim figure: a man of letters and a librettist, he came from Berkshire and died in Cambridge.

DRAKE'S DRUM

Words by
Henry Newbolt

Music by
C. Villiers Stanford

Lyrics:
Drake he's in his hammock and a thou-sand mile a-way, (Cap-tain art thou sleeping there be-low?) Slung a-tween the round shot in Nom-bre Di-os Bay, And dream-ing all the time of Ply-mouth Hoe. Yon-der looms the is-land,

26

Drake's Drum

low?) Rov - ing tho' his death fell, he

went with heart at ease, And dream - ing all the time of Ply - mouth

Hoe. 'Take my drum to En - gland,

hang it by the shore, Strike it when your pow - der's run - ning

low; If the Dons sight De - von, I'll

28

Drake's Drum

quit the port of Hea - ven, And drum them up the Chan-nel as we drumm'd them long a -

largamente

go.' Drake he's in his

ham-mock till the great Ar - ma - das come,

(Cap - tain, art thou sleep - ing there be - low?)

Slung a-tween the round shot, list -'ning for the drum, And dream - ing all the

Land of Hope and Glory

time of Ply-mouth Hoe. Call him on the deep sea,

Call him up the Sound, Call him when ye sail to meet the

foe; Where the old trade's ply - ing and the old flag fly - ing, They shall

find him ware and wa - king, As they found him long a -

go!

DRAKE'S DRUM

1. Drake, he's in his hammock and a thousand mile away,
     (Captain, art thou sleeping there below?)
   Slung atween the round shot in Nombre Dios Bay,
     And dreaming all the time of Plymouth Hoe.
   Yonder looms the island, yonder lie the ships,
     With sailor lads a dancing heel an' toe,
   And the shore-lights flashing, and the night-tide dashing,
     He sees it all so plainly as he saw it long ago.

2. Drake he was a Devon man, and ruled the Devon seas,
     (Captain, art thou sleeping there below?)
   Roving tho' his death fell, he went with heart at ease,
     And dreaming all the time of Plymouth Hoe.
   'Take my drum to England, hang it by the shore,
     Strike it when your powder's running low;
   If the Dons sight Devon, I'll quit the port of Heaven,
     And drum them up the Channel as we drumm'd them long ago.'

3. Drake he's in his hammock till the great Armadas come,
     (Captain, art thou sleeping there below?)
   Slung atween the round shot, listening for the drum,
     And dreaming all the time of Plymouth Hoe.
   Call him on the deep sea, call him up the Sound,
     Call him when ye sail to meet the foe;
   Where the old trade's plying and the old flag flying,
     They shall find him ware and waking, as they found him long ago!

The verses in the ballad as printed above are in standard English; Newbolt's poem was written in fruity Devon dialect, and singers who would like to attempt a rustic rendition should use the text below:

1. Drake he's in his hammock an' a thousand mile away,
     (Capten, art tha sleepin' there below?)
   Slung atween the round shot in Nombre Dios Bay,
     An' dreamin' arl the time o' Plymouth Hoe.
   Yarnder lümes the Island, yarnder lie the ships,
     Wi' sailor lads a dancin' heel an' toe,
   An' the shore-lights flashin', an' the night-tide dashin',
     He sees et arl so plainly as he saw et long ago.

2. Drake he was a Devon man, an' rüled the Devon seas,
     (Capten, art tha sleepin' there below?)
   Rovin' tho' his death fell, he went wi' heart at ease,
     An' dreamin' arl the time o' Plymouth Hoe.
   'Take my drum to England, hang et by the shore,
     Strike et when your powder's runnin' low;
   If the Dons sight Devon, I'll quit the port o' Heaven,
     An' drum them up the Channel as we drumm'd them long ago.'

3. Drake he's in his hammock till the great Armadas come,
   (Capten, art tha sleepin' there below?)
   Slung atween the round shot, listenin' for the drum,
   An' dreamin' arl the time o' Plymouth Hoe.
   Call him on the deep sea, call him up the Sound,
   Call him when ye sail to meet the foe;
   Where the old trade's plyin' and the old flag's flyin'
   They shall find him ware an' wakin', as they found him long ago!

This song is perhaps now the best-remembered ballad of both poet and composer. It celebrates Queen Elizabeth's favourite admiral and buccaneer, who singed the King of Spain's beard and looted his gold in the days before the difference between national defence and piracy was defined.

Sir Henry John Newbolt (1862-1938), the 'nautical Kipling' as Walter de la Mare christened him, flowered mightily in the Edwardian period and his verse is redolent of it. His best-known collections of maritime pieces were published between 1897 and 1912, and they served to perpetuate the Jolly Jack Tar industry which Charles Dibdin had launched a century before. The son of a clergyman, Newbolt hailed from Staffordshire — a county entirely land-locked — but he went to Clifton College where the proximity of the great port of Bristol must have excited his passion for the sea. He secured a First at Corpus Christi, Oxford, and became a barrister, a profession he soon abandoned for naval literature, gaining a considerable if fugitive reputation as novelist, poet and historian.

A formidable and fecund establishment musician, Sir Charles Villiers Stanford (1852-1924) was born in Dublin and obtained an organ scholarship at Queens' College, Cambridge. He subsequently became organist at Trinity, studied in Germany and carried off sundry academic honours of which the professorship of music at Cambridge was the most prestigious. An accomplished pianist and conductor, it was however as composer that he burgeoned. His name was made when Tennyson chose him to write music for a production of *Queen Mary* at the Lyceum, and he poured forth a cataract of respectable works: seven forgotten operas, oratorios (those necessary Victorian accomplishments), odes and cantatas, psalms, services and masses as well as a fine 'Stabat Mater', six symphonies and assorted overtures, concertos, organ works, chamber music and songs. Of the last, his arrangements of Irish melodies (see the note to 'Trottin' to the Fair' on page 74) and his settings of Newbolt's maritime verses are now the best known. Of his more ambitious *oeuvre*, his magnificent church music is worth more attention than it receives today.

Stanford's stirring setting of 'Drake's Drum' relies heavily upon an imitation of a drum beating in the piano part and a folk-song rhythm replete with 'Scotch snaps' in the vocal line. A spirited performance will still be effective and reflect the composer's sure-footed technique.

The original song front of 'The Trumpeter', 1904

THE TRUMPETER

Words by
J. Francis Barron

Music by
J. Airlie Dix

Trum-pe-ter, what are you sound-ing now? (Is it the call I'm seek-ing?) 'You'll know the call,' said the Trum-pe-ter tall, 'When my trum-pet goes a speak-in'. I'm rous-in' 'em up, I'm wak-in' 'em up, The tents are a-stir in the val-ley, And there's

34

The Trumpeter

no more sleep, with the sun's first peep, For I'm sound-in' the old "Re - veil - le!" Rise up!' said the Trumpeter tall.

Trum - pe - ter, what are you sound - ing now? (Is it the call I'm seek - ing?) 'Can't mis - take the call,' said the Trum - pe - ter tall, 'When my trum - pet goes a - speak - in.' I'm urg - in' 'em on,' they're scamp - er - in' on,___ There's a drum - min' of hoofs like___ thun - der. There's a

Land of Hope and Glory

mad - 'nin' shout as the sab-res flash out, For I'm sound - ing the "Charge" no_ won -

der! And it's *Hell'* said the Trumpeter tall.

Trum - pe-ter, what are you sound - ing now? (Is it the call I'm

seek - ing?) 'Luck-y for you if you hear it at all, For my trum - pet's but faint - ly

speak - in'. I'm call - in' 'em home! _ Come home! come home! Tread light o'er the dead in the

The Trumpeter

37

THE TRUMPETER

1. Trumpeter, what are you sounding now?
   (Is it the call I'm seeking?)
   'You'll know the call,' said the Trumpeter tall,
   'When my trumpet goes a-speakin'.
   I'm rousin' 'em up, I'm wakin' 'em up,
   The tents are a-stir in the valley,
   And there's no more sleep, with the sun's first peep,
   For I'm soundin' the old "Reveille"!
   Rise up!' said the Trumpeter tall.

2. Trumpeter, what are you sounding now?
   (Is it the call I'm seeking?)
   'Can't mistake the call,' said the Trumpeter tall, ,
   'When my trumpet goes a-speakin'.
   I'm urgin' 'em on, they're scamperin' on,
   There's a drummin' of hoofs like thunder.
   There's a mad'nin' shout as the sabres flash out,
   For I'm soundin' the "Charge" -- no wonder!
   And it's *Hell*!' said the Trumpeter tall.

3. Trumpeter, what are you sounding now?
   (Is it the call I'm seeking?)
   'Lucky for you if you hear it at all,
   For my trumpet's but faintly speakin'.
   I'm callin' 'em home! Come home! come home!
   Tread light o'er the dead in the valley,
   Who are lyin' around face down to the ground,
   And they can't hear me sound the "Rally".
   But they'll hear it again in a grand refrain,
   When Gabriel sounds the last "Rally".'

For some strange reason 'The Trumpeter' has survived in popular memory as one of the great ballad hits of the Edwardian period; it was certainly very popular but not more so than dozens of others of the same type. Perhaps the robust rendering on record by Peter Dawson, sold by the many thousands in the 'twenties and 'thirties, won for it a celebrity it did not achieve in its own time.

It is interesting to see that the line in the second stanza, ' "And it's *Hell*!" said the Trumpeter tall' is marked as optional in performance, as is the milder equivalent in the first stanza. The reason for this is clearly to avoid offending nervous singers or, perhaps more to the point, nervous audiences. The lyricist Harold Simpson, author of *A Century of Ballads*, recalls being asked by a music shop to change two lines of his verse in 'A Chip of the Old Block' which had become popular in W.H. Squire's setting. The lines were 'The sea's the very devil, and/A woman's just as bad!' The objection was that many singers felt that they could not render them at chapel teas, and sales of the ballad were suffering as a result. A deft change to 'The sea's the very divil' removed the offence. Simpson also remarked ruefully that sales of 'The Corporal's Ditty' were hampered by the single use of the word 'damn'.

John Francis Barron (1870-?) was a Londoner who wrote the words of a number of popular ballads of a military and naval character, including 'My Old Shako' (which appears on page 48) and 'Trooper Johnny Ludlow'. *Who's Who in Music* of the time had little to say about him, apart from the intriguing fact that he 'travelled extensively'.

The composer, J. Airlie Dix, is another shadowy figure. Other successful songs of his were 'The Abbott of Guise' and 'A Jolly Old Cavalier'. His attractive setting of Barron's verse makes much play with the bugle echoes heard in the opening bars allied to a powerful march rhythm. A fine strophic song, 'The Trumpeter' repays a red-blooded rendition.

THE OLD SUPERB

Words by
Henry Newbolt

Music by
C. Villiers Stanford

The Old Superb

'Old Su - perb' is old and foul and slow; But the French are gone to Mar - ti - nique, and

Nel-son's on the trail, And__ where he goes the 'Old Su-perb' must go.

So West-ward ho! for Trin- i - dad, and__ East-ward ho! for Spain, And

'Ship a-hoy!'_____ a hun- dred times a day; Round the world if

need be, and round the world a-gain With a lame duck lag-ging, lag - ging all the

Land of Hope and Glory

way.   The

'Old Su-perb' was bar-na-cled and green as grass be-low,   Her sticks   were on - ly   fit for __ stir - ring __

grog;   The   pride of all her mid-ship-men was   si - lent long a - go,   And long   a - go   they

ceased   to heave the __ log,   Four year out from home she was, and ne'er a week in port, And

no thing save   the   guns   a - board her   bright;   But Cap-tain Keats he knew the game, and

The Old Superb

swore to share the sport, For he ne- ver yet came in too late to fight. So

West-ward ho! for Trin - i - dad, and East-ward ho! for Spain, And 'Ship a-hoy!' a

hun - dred times a day; Round the world if need be, and

round the world a-gain With a lame duck lag-ging, lag-ging all the way.

'Now up my lads,' the Cap-tain cried, 'for

43

Land of Hope and Glory

sure the case were hard   If long- est   out   were   first to__ fall__ be - hind;   A -

loft,   a-loft with stud-ding sails, and lash them on the yard,   For__ night   and   day   the   trades   are driv - ing__

blind.'   So   all day long and all day long be - hind the fleet we crept,   And how   we   fret - ted

none   but Nel - son guessed;   But   ev-'ry night the 'Old Su-perb' she sail'd when o-thers slept, Till   we

ran   the French   to earth   with all   the   rest.   O   'twas West-ward ho!   for

The Old Superb

Trin-i-dad, and East-ward ho! for Spain, and 'Ship a-hoy!' a hun-dred times a day; Round the world if need be, and round the world a-gain, With a lame duck, a lame duck a lag-ging, lag-ging, lag-ging all the way!

rallentando

Presto

45

THE OLD SUPERB

1. The wind was rising easterly, the morning sky was blue,
   The Straits before us open'd wide and free;
   We look'd towards the Admiral, where high the Peter flew,
   And all our hearts were dancing like the sea.
   The French are gone to Martinique with four and twenty sail,
   The 'Old Superb' is old and foul and slow;
   But the French are gone to Martinique, and Nelson's on the trail,
   And where he goes the 'Old Superb' must go.

   So Westward ho! for Trinidad, and Eastward ho! for Spain,
   And 'Ship a-hoy!' a hundred times a day;
   Round the world if need be, and round the world again
   With a lame duck lagging, lagging all the way.

2. The 'Old Superb' was barnacled and green as grass below,
   Her sticks were only fit for stirring grog;
   The pride of all her midshipmen was silent long ago,
   And long ago they ceased to heave the log,
   Four year out from home she was, and ne'er a week in port,
   And nothing save the guns aboard her bright;
   But Captain Keats he knew the game, and swore to share the sport,
   For he never yet came in too late to fight.

   So Westward ho! for Trinidad, *etc.*

3. 'Now up, my lads,' the Captain cried, 'for sure the case were hard
   If longest out were first to fall behind;
   Aloft, aloft with studding sails, and lash them on the yard,
   For night and day the trades are driving blind.'
   So all day long and all day long behind the fleet we crept,
   And how we fretted none but Nelson guessed;
   But ev'ry night the 'Old Superb' she sail'd when others slept,
   Till we ran the French to earth with all the rest.

   O 'twas Westward ho! for Trinidad, and Eastward ho! for Spain,
   And 'Ship a-hoy!' a hundred times a day;
   Round the world if need be, and round the world again,
   With a lame duck, a lame duck a-lagging, lagging, lagging all the way!

So long as there is a rollicking baritone in Britain, 'The Old Superb' and its companion *Songs of the Sea*, like 'Drake's Drum' and 'Homeward Bound' by Newbolt and Stanford, will continue in the repertoire. There are short biographies of the poet and composer on page 32.

With its catchy refrain — 'So Westward ho! for Trinidad!' — this ballad enjoyed an enormous success in the early years of the century and was bellowed out in many a school singing class between the wars. There its steady measure and irresistible 'yo-ho-ho-ishness' made it a firm favourite. One cannot help feeling that a school choir would have enjoyed the music teacher's 'hurry music' in the final bars enormously too.

VOCAL DUETS, etc., Standard and Popular.

Price Two Shillings Each, Net, except where otherwise marked.

TWO SOPRANOS.

Go, pretty Rose (in G)	Theo. Marzials
Hark, the Lark (in F)	A. Delbruck
Spring and Love (in A♭)	M. W. Balfe
Trust her not	Theo. Marzials
Who is Sylvia (in G)	F. E. Gambogi

Childland. Cycle. Price 5/-

SOPRANO and MEZZO SOPRANO.

Coming Home	Arthur Sullivan
Down the Vale (in C)	F. L. Moir
Echoes	"
Heralds of Spring (in A♭)	Waddington Cooke
The Shepherd's Roundelay (in G)	R. H. Walthew
Sweet Wild Birds	F. L. Moir
Who is Sylvia? (A♭)	Harper Kearton

Childland. Cycle. Price 5/-

SOPRANO and CONTRALTO.

An Evening Song	V. Gabriel
At Last	Arthur Fagge
By the Waters	Stephen Adams
Down the Vale (in G)	F. L. Moir
Echoes	"
Excelsior (in C)	M. W. Balfe
Four Sunbeams	Liza Lehmann
Heralds of Spring (in A♭)	Waddington Cooke
I Fly like a Bird	Arthur Foote
In Springtime	Ernest Newton
It was a Lover	Mary Carmichael
Love and Time	Hermann Löhr
Love has turned his face away	Arthur Foote
Love in her Boat (From "Rival Poets")	Edward Germann
A Madrigal in May	Ernest Newton
Una sera d'amore	Campana
Clear and Cool	
The Mermaids	
See how the Day	Price 2/- each, or the Set of Six complete, 4/- net.
The Sisters	A. H. Behrend
Sleep, Baby, sleep	
Violets	
Where the Violets grow (From "The Little Sunbonnet")	Hermann Löhr
Who is Sylvia? (G)	Harper Kearton
Wicked Cupid	H. Trotère

The Village. Cycle. Price 4/- .. R. H. Walthew

SOPRANO and TENOR.

Break, Diviner Light (in F)	Frances Allitsen
Dear Love of mine (in F) (From "Nadeshda")	A. Goring Thomas
Down the Sunlit Stream	J. L. Molloy
Down the Stream (in A♭)	L. Denza
Good Night, dear heart (in E♭)	Ernest Newton
It was a Lover (in F)	R. H. Walthew
Love of a Friend	S. Liddle
Nights of Music (in D)	F. H. Cowen
Rose and Lily (Vicar of Wakefield)	Liza Lehmann
Snowdrops (No. 2 edition)	Liza Lehmann
Songs of Twilight	J. L. Roeckel
Weep ye no more (in E♭)	Waddington Cooke
Why ask me if I love (From "The Wooden Spoon")	Hope Temple

SOPRANO and BARITONE.

A Daffodil and a Willow Tree	Thomas F. Dunhill
Allah be with us (in C) (From "A Lover in Damascus")	A. Woodforde-Finden
At Love's Beginning (in A♭)	Liza Lehmann
By the Waters	Stephen Adams
De Lady Moon (Plantation)	A. S. Gatty
Down the Vale (in G)	F. L. Moir
Glide to thy Rest	Hamilton Aidé
Happy Day	Edward German
Heralds of Spring (in G)	Waddington Cooke
Hurry up, Pompey (Plantation)	A. S. Gatty
In Springtime (in G and A)	Ernest Newton
Is it the Wind of the Dawn (in A)	C. V. Stanford
Love in the evening Breeze	Marie Horne
North and South	Teresa del Riego
Regret	Thomas F. Dunhill
The Pitcher	H. Arnold Smith
The Shepherd's Roundelay (in G)	R. H. Walthew
Who is Sylvia? (A♭)	Harper Kearton
Wicked Cupid	H. Trotère

Three Vocal Duets. Price 2/6 .. Harry Farjeon

SOPRANO and BASS.

At Love's Beginning (in A♭)	Liza Lehmann
In Springtime (in G and A)	Ernest Newton
Regret	Thomas F. Dunhill
Wicked Cupid	H. Trotère

TWO MEZZO SOPRANOS.

Go, pretty Rose (in F)	Theo. Marzials
Hark, the Lark (in E♭)	"
Heigho	J. Spaxforth
It was a Lover	Theo. Marzials
Trust her not	M. W. Balfe
Under the Greenwood Tree	Theo. Marzials
Unto the Holly	"
Weep ye no more	"
Who is Sylvia (in F)	"
Winter's Song	"

MEZZO and CONTRALTO.

Down the Vale (in F)	F. L. Moir
Excelsior (in B♭)	M. W. Balfe
Fear no more	Theo. Marzials
The Golden Goose	Ernest Newton
The Mermaids	A. H. Behrend
The Shepherd's Roundelay (in F)	R. H. Walthew

MEZZO and BARITONE.

Allah be with us (in B♭) (From "A Lover in Damascus")	A. Woodforde-Finden
The Crafty Crocodile .. (From "Peter Pan")	Joan Trevalsa
Down the Stream (in F)	L. Denza
Down the Vale (in F)	F. L. Moir
Love in the evening Breeze	Marie Horne
Regret	Thomas F. Dunhill
Silver-Land	Frank L. Moir
The Golden Goose	Ernest Newton
The Harbour Lights (in B)	W. H. Squire
Love enthroned (in D) (From "Songs of Love and Spring")	Liza Lehmann
The Shepherd's Roundelay (in F)	R. H. Walthew
Weep ye no more (in C)	Waddington Cooke
Who's for the Fields (C and D)	Blanche Gaston-Murray

TWO CONTRALTOS.

Sweet Content	J. Blumenthal

CONTRALTO and TENOR.

Where the Violets grow (From "The Little Sunbonnet")	Hermann Löhr
Who is Sylvia? (A♭)	Harper Kearton

CONTRALTO and BARITONE.

Allah be with us (in B♭) (From "A Lover in Damascus")	A. Woodforde-Finden
Break, Diviner Light (in E♭)	Frances Allitsen
The Crafty Crocodile.. (From "Peter Pan")	Joan Trevalsa
Good Luck and Bad	W. H. Squire
Good Night, dear heart (in C)	Ernest Newton
The Harbour Lights (in A)	W. H. Squire
In Love's Domain	R. H. Walthew
It was a Lover (in D)	A. W. Juncker
I was Dreaming	Liza Lehmann
Love enthroned (in C) (From "Songs of Love and Spring")	Marie Horne
Love's Invocation	F. H. Cowen
Nights of Music (in B♭)	W. H. Squire
The Singing Lesson	Liza Lehmann
Snowdrops (No. 1 edition)	A. Delbruck
Spring and Love (in D)	Waddington Cooke
Weep ye no more (in C)	Harriet Young
Where the Roses are	Augustus Barratt
Won't you buy?	V. Gabriel
Yet once again	

TWO TENORS.

Spring and Love (in A♭)	A. Delbruck

TENOR and BARITONE.

The Chamois Hunters	J. L. Hatton
Excelsior (in D)	M. W. Balfe
The Fishermen (in F)	Gabussi
The Golden Goose	Ernest Newton
In Springtime (in G and A)	Ernest Newton
O Mistress mine	W. Kingsley Tarpey
Sweet Wild Birds	F. L. Moir
The Gendarmes	Offenbach
The Lovers	H. Lane Wilson
Watchman! What of the Night?	J. Sarjeant
Who is Sylvia? (A♭)	Harper Kearton
Wicked Cupid	H. Trotère

TENOR and BASS.

Watchman! What of the Night?	J. Sarjeant
Wicked Cupid	H. Trotère

TRIOS.

Land of Hope and Glory (Arranged by Arthur Fagge. Two Sopranos, and Contralto) Price 3d.	Edward Elgar
My Embarrassing Distress (From "Rival Poets")	Edward German
The Sea hath its Pearls. (Ladies' Voices)	Elsie Horne
Wind Flowers.* (Ladies' Voices)	Arthur Somervell

*(In Old and Tonic Sol fa Notations, price 1/- net.)

The back cover of a Boosey ballad, 1904

MY OLD SHAKO

Words by
J. Francis Barron

Music by
H. Trotère

My Old Shako

kiss from me Be-neath my old shak-o! ____ When first she took a kiss from me Be

neath my old shak-o! ____ Heigh - ho! Ma-ny a year a-go, ____ We rode a-long to geth-er, You and

I, my old shak-o. Faith! We turned the heads of half the pret-ty girls we used to

know, ____ Ten, twen-ty, thir-ty, for-ty, fif-ty years a - go!

AFTER THE VOICE

49

Land of Hope and Glory

I re-col-lect, my old shak-o, How once you saved my pate ___ E-gad! 'Twas in my maid-en fight, Way back in fif-ty-eight; ___ When bri-dle arm was hang-ing loose, And my head look'd fair to go, ___ 'Twas then I thank'd my luck-y stars I wore an old shak-o. ___ 'Twas then I thank'd my luck-y stars I wore an old shak-o. ___

50

My Old Shako

Land of Hope and Glory

an - swers 'Roll,' But nev - er a one comes back. ___ Then let this be ___ my ep - i - taph, When-

-e'er they lay me low ___ 'Here lies a jol - ly Light Dra-goon, Who loved his old shak-

-o! ___ Here lies a jol - ly Light Dra-goon, Who loved his old shak - o!' ___

Heigh - ho!

Hail, ___ rain or snow ___ Here's a health to all the pret-ty girls we used to

My Old Shako

MY OLD SHAKO

1. I mind the day, my old shako,
   When first you graced my head;
   What time I wore my sabre-tasche,
   My spurs, and jacket red.
   I mind a dainty little lass
   Whose cheeks were all a-glow,
   When first she took a kiss from me
   Beneath my old shako!

   Heigh-ho! Many a year ago,
   We rode along together,
   You and I, my old shako.
   Faith!
   We turned the heads of half the pretty girls we used to know,
   Ten, twenty, thirty, forty, fifty years ago!

2. I recollect, my old shako,
   How once you saved my pate —
   Egad! 'twas in my maiden fight,
   Way back in fifty-eight;
   When bridle arm was hanging loose,
   And my head look'd fair to go,
   'Twas then I thank'd my lucky stars
   I wore an old shako.

   Heigh-ho! Many a year ago,
   We took our scars together,
   You and I, my old shako.
   Faith!
   We didn't care a button if the odds were on the foe,
   Ten, twenty, thirty, forty, fifty years ago!

3. I'm waiting now, my old shako,
   The Call to Bivouac;
   Where ev'ry beggar answers 'Roll,'
   But never a one comes back.
   Then let this be my epitaph,
   When e'er they lay me low —
   'Here lies a jolly Light Dragoon,
   Who loved his old shako!'

   Heigh-ho! Hail, rain or snow —
   Here's a health to all the pretty girls we used to know!
   And here's to ev'ry soldier man who wore an old shako,
   Ten, twenty, thirty, forty, fifty years ago!

'My Old Shako' was Trotère's most popular song, selling well over two million copies. It achieved such celebrity that, as Harold Simpson records in *A Century of Ballads*, a concert manager asked a singer *not* to perform it, 'as the public must be tired of it'. Hesitantly, the singer agreed but did give it as an encore; whereupon the encore was promptly encored.

Henri Trotère appears in his photographs as a solid-looking man with luxuriant handle-bar moustaches; it is therefore no surprise to learn that he was really Henry Trotter (1855-?). At one time a player in the Royal Aquarium orchestra, he later became a most prolific ballad-writer who had a number of huge successes in late Victorian and Edwardian times. Among them were 'In Old Madrid', his first big winner, but in fact his twenty-ninth song, which had the dubious distinction of achieving twenty-eight pirated editions in America. Others included 'Go to Sea' which Trotère dreamed up on the top deck of an omnibus, and 'The Deathless Army' (which is included in *Just A Song at Twilight* by the present editors). Oddly enough, Henry Trotter was almost exactly contemporaneous with Dr Thomas Henry Yorke Trotter, a prominent musical educationist who must have viewed the activities of his popular namesake with mixed feelings.

There is a note on the lyricist, J. Francis Barron on page 39.

The military flourishes in Trotère's ritornellos help to move this song along splendidly. In case the pianist fails to spot them, the composer has marked them carefully 'Brass', 'Lights Out', 'Stables' and so on. The setting has a fine jaunty swing to it, and a spirited baritone performance can still thrill an audience.

DRAKE GOES WEST

Words by
P. J. O'Reilly

Music by
Wilfrid Sanderson

Molto allegro marziale *(with much vigour)*

Drake is go-ing West, lad, His ships are in the bay,

dim. a tempo *sotto voce e sempre staccato*

Five and twen-ty sail all told, Rea-dy for the fray! Oh! hear it pass from

lip to lip 'Drake __ is off a-gain!' Aye, Drake's a-way at break o' day, To

56

Drake Goes West

Più vivace

sweep ___ (or) to sweep the Span - ish Main! Then here's to the Span-ish Main— And here's ___ to the foe! And here's to Drake and his mer-ry, mer-ry men, Who'll ne-ver come back to Devon a - gain, Till they've laid ___ the en - e - my low!

57

Land of Hope and Glory

Drake is go-ing West, lad, You'd like to go, would you? Then go you shall to

share the fight And the glo - ry too! Be - fore our men the foe shall fall

Like ___ the sick-led grain, For Drake is go-ing West-ward, lad, To sweep ___ (to

___ the Span-ish Main! ___ Then here's to the Spanish Main — And

here's ___ to the foe! And here's to Drake and his mer-ry, mer-ry men, Who'll ne-ver come back to

58

Drake Goes West

Devon a-gain, Till they've laid _____ the en-e-my low!

Some are go-ing West, lad, Who'll ne'er win home a-gain—

Some will sleep their long, long sleep, 'Neath the Span – ish Main! But

what-so-ev-er be our fate— Come what may, say I, With

60

DRAKE GOES WEST

1. Drake is going West, lad,
   His ships are in the bay,
   Five and twenty sail all told,
   Ready for the fray!
   Oh! hear it pass from lip to lip
   'Drake is off again!'
   Aye, Drake's away at break o' day,
   To sweep the Spanish Main!

   Then here's to the Spanish Main —
   And here's to the foe!
   And here's to Drake and his merry, merry men,
   Who'll never come back to Devon again,
   Till they've laid the enemy low!

2. Drake is going West, lad,
   You'd like to go, would you?
   Then go you shall to share the fight
   And the glory too!
   Before our men the foe shall fall
   Like the sickled grain,
   For Drake is going Westward, lad,
   To sweep the Spanish Main!

   Then here's to the Spanish Main *etc.*

3. Some are going West, lad,
   Who'll ne'er win home again —
   Some will sleep their long, long sleep,
   'Neath the Spanish Main!
   But whatsoever be our fate —
   Come what may, say I,
   With Drake we'll go, for Drake we'll fight,
   With Drake we'll win or die!

   Then here's to the Spanish Main *etc.*

Another contribution to the musical celebration of Sir Francis Drake, this song although immensely popular could not rival 'Drake's Drum'. The reason is not far to seek: in spite of Sanderson's excellent setting the generalized verse of the shadowy P.J. O'Reilly is no match for the swaggering yet moving poetry of Sir Henry Newbolt.

Wilfrid Ernest Sanderson (1878-1935) was a vicar's son, like a remarkably large number of the authors and composers in this book. He was born in Ipswich and on leaving the City of London School was prepared for a musical career by Sir Frederick Bridge. After a couple of years in business he decided to become a professional musician and established himself as organist and choirmaster in Doncaster at a time when the musical life of the North of England was robust and rewarding. In his thirties he was winning plaudits as a song-writer, and he teamed up with the veteran lyricist Fred E. Weatherly to reproduce many immensely successful ballads, several of which may be found in this collection.

In Sanderson's best 'Up from Somerset' vein, this song is typically workmanlike and beautifully set for the voice. Notice how effectively the composer 'sweeps the Spanish Main' with a firm broom-stroke.

WON'T YOU JOIN THE ARMY?

Words by
George R. Sims

Music by
J. M. Glover

When the fair-ies are not danc-ing in the moon-lit glade and dell, They are
bu - sy put-ting mor-tals un der-neath their fai-ry spell, And a fai - ry boy who wan-ders o'er a

Land of Hope and Glory

world at work and play Longs to put the boys of Brit-ain 'neath his fai-ry spell to day. 'Neath the

spell of Eng-land's hon-our one who's Brit-ish born him self Wants to hold you, for I've

told you Puck's a lit-tle Eng-lish elf. He is going to fight for Eng-land and he

wants you ev-'ry one To join the lit-tle Arm-y that is out a-gainst the Hun. ____

CHORUS

Won't you join the Arm - y? Won't you come with me? Won't you come with

Won't You Join the Army?

me, boys, to Ber - lin on the Spree? ___ Say good - bye to Kate or Nan, She'll be

proud that you're a man. Won't you, won't you, won't you come? Won't you, won't you come and join?

Won't you won't you, won't you, won't you come and join with me? ___ me? ___

Land of Hope and Glory

Of _ all the gal - lant deeds you've done, we've heard in Fai - ry - land, We _

know that ne'er a foe of old your val - our could with-stand. But _ now there's dan-ger on the sea and

dan - ger on the shore, That _ Brit-ain in her is - land pride has ne - ver known be - fore. The _

land that no in - va - der's foot has trod since Har - old's day Is _ threat-n'd by a fo - reign horde who

help - less wo - men slay! Then _ up for wo-men, bairns and home, ye men of Brit - ish blood, To

Won't You Join the Army?

pluck the Ger - man ea - gle's crest and dam the Ger - man flood. _____

CHORUS

Won't you join the Arm - y? Won't you come with me? Won't you ral - ly round the flag a -

- cross the North - ern Sea? _____ Say good - bye to Kate or Nan, She'll be proud that you're a

man. Won't you, won't you, won't you come? Won't you, won't you come and join?

Won't you, won't you won't you, won't you come and join with me? _____ me? _____

WON'T YOU JOIN THE ARMY?

1. When the fairies are not dancing in the moonlit glade and dell,
    They are busy putting mortals underneath their fairy spell,
    And a fairy boy who wanders o'er a world at work and play
    Longs to put the boys of Britain 'neath his fairy spell today.
    'Neath the spell of England's honour one who's British born himself
    Wants to hold you, for I've told you Puck's a little English elf.
    He is going to fight for England and he wants you ev'ry one
    To join the little Army that is out against the Hun.

    Won't you join the Army? Won't you come with me?
    Won't you come with me, boys, to Berlin on the Spree?
    Say goodbye to Kate or Nan,
    She'll be proud that you're a man.
    Won't you, won't you, won't you come? Won't you, won't you come and join?
    Won't you, won't you, won't you, won't you come and join with me?

2. Of all the gallant deeds you've done, we've heard in Fairyland,
    We know that ne'er a foe of old your valour could withstand.
    But now there's danger on the sea and danger on the shore,
    That Britain in her island pride has never known before.
    The Land that no invader's foot has trod since Harold's day
    Is threaten'd by a foreign horde who helpless women slay!
    Then up for women, bairns and home, ye men of British blood,
    To pluck the German eagle's crest and dam the German flood.

    Won't you join the Army? Won't you come with me?
    Won't you rally round the flag across the Northern Sea?
    Say goodbye to Kate or Nan,
    She'll be proud that you're a man.
    Won't you, won't you, won't you come? Won't you, won't you come and join?
    Won't you, won't you, won't you, won't you come and join with me?

The very curious lyric of this ballad of 1914 exhibits an unreality at the outbreak of war that is scarcely credible now, and suggests how violent a shock the horrors of Flanders were to be to the British middle class. The line in the first stanza, 'He is going to fight for England and he wants you ev'ry one,' is a borrowed snatch from the patriotic ditty 'Private Tommy Atkins' by Henry Hamilton and S. Potter which had been given temporary fame by the singer Hayden Coffin.

A people's poet if ever there was one, George Robert Sims (1847-1922) is not likely to figure in any history of literature. Yet, such narrative verses as 'In the Workhouse: Christmas Day' (the famous 'Christmas Day in the Workhouse'), 'Billy's Rose' and 'The Lifeboat' were written with reforming passion and won an enormous public on both sides of the Atlantic. Sims called himself 'Dagonet' for such effusions, but he was also a popular journalist with a column that ran for forty-five years, a playwright, novelist and noted breeder of bulldogs. He is not celebrated as a song-writer, and this lyric perhaps shows why.

James Mackay Glover (1861-1931) was an Irishman who became variously director of music at Drury Lane, manager of the Theatre Royal, Plymouth, and mayor of Bexhill-on-Sea. He also worked as a music critic and correspondent for several newspapers and wrote the music for hundreds of songs as well as dances and ballet music. In this ballad Glover takes care to throw the audience off balance with his military introduction to what at first seems to be a song about fairy dances. Soon enough, though, the real nature of the song is revealed and the dance is seen to be none other than the military two-step!

2

A Garden Hard by Heaven

or, Songs of the Countryside

TROTTIN' TO THE FAIR

Words by
Alfred Perceval Graves

Music arranged by
C. Villiers Stanford

A Garden Hard by Heaven

By her gen - tle breath - in' Whis - per'd past my ear,

And her white arms wreath - in' Warm a - round me here.

Thus on Dob - bin's back I dis - coursed the dar - ling,

Till up - on our track Leaped a mon - grel snar - ling;

72

Trottin' to the Fair

'Ah,' says Moll, 'I'm fright - en'd, fright - en'd That the po - ny'll start!' And her

pret - ty hands she tight - en'd round_____ my hap - py heart:

Till I axed her 'May I Steal a kiss or so?'_____ And my Mol - ly's grey eye

Did - n't an - swer no._____

73

TROTTIN' TO THE FAIR

1. Trottin' to the fair
   Me and Moll Molony,
   Seated I declare
   On a single pony.
   How am I to know that
   Molly's safe behind,
   With our heads in oh, that awk'ard, awk'ard way inclined?

   By her gentle breathin'
   Whisper'd past my ear,
   And her white arms wreathin'
   Warm around me here.

2. Thus on Dobbin's back
   I discoursed the darling,
   Till upon our track
   Leaped a mongrel snarling;
   'Ah,' says Moll, 'I'm frighten'd, frighten'd
   That the pony'll start!'
   And her pretty hands she tighten'd round my happy heart:

   Till I axed her, 'May I
   Steal a kiss or so?'
   And my Molly's grey eye
   Didn't answer no.

From the mid-eighteenth century onwards Ireland provided a seemingly inexhaustible fountain of rustic tunes that could be prettied up in melting arrangements and adorned with sentimental lyrics for the parlour. It was the poet Thomas Moore who turned what had been a pleasant dilettantish hobby into an industry: his volumes of *Irish Melodies* which were published from 1807 to 1835 released a flood of enchanting songs, not all of them Irish by any means despite Moore's confident attributions. For many years they were uncritically accepted as genuine traditional songs, and the most famous, 'The Last Rose of Summer', 'Oft in the Stilly Night', 'The Minstrel Boy', 'Believe Me If All Those Endearing Young Charms' and many others sold literally by the million to besotted amateur vocalists the world over. Later in the century when scholars were beginning to find more merit in the originals than in the polite reworkings, Moore's improvements received many harsh words. But he had started something that was very difficult to stop, and, following the practice of dozens of Victorian song-writers, a century after Moore had begun it all, even such a thoroughly respectable musician as Sir Charles Stanford was composing winning settings of traditional Irish tunes with newly-minted words tacked on. Indeed, some of his very popular versions, perhaps rather more faithful to the originals, were of ballads first resurrected by Moore. The most successful of Stanford's settings were 'Father O'Flynn', 'Trottin' to the Fair' and 'My Love's an Arbutus', and the first singers of the day speedily adopted them for their repertoires. Among their exponents were Sir Charles Santley and Plunket Greene. The latter regarded 'Trottin' to the Fair' virtually as his own: 'It is a common idea', he said, 'that a humorous song is on a lower scale than a tragic or a sentimental one. . . . A song can be light and amusing and meant to laugh at, and yet superlatively good. "Trottin' to the Fair" is just as much a masterpiece in its own line as Schubert's "Doppelgänger".' Stanford also produced original songs in the Irish idiom: his song cycle *Cushendall* is an example. He was not alone either in adapting Irish tunes for Edwardian performers: Hamilton Harty and Arthur Somervell were among many tillers in a fertile field. There is a short biography of Stanford on page 32.

Alfred Perceval Graves (1846-1931) was the lyric-writer most involved in the Irish song revival, producing polite rusticities for a number of composers. The son of the Bishop of Limerick, he came from a line of professional men, scholars and divines. His first publication, *Songs of Killarney*, appeared whilst he was a Home Office clerk. He moved on to a long career as an inspector of schools in England, his sideline being the production of words to old Irish and Welsh tunes. Although his knowledge of the old Irish and Welsh languages was but a smattering, he is said to have conveyed the spirit of the originals rather well.

Accompanying the helter-skelter lyrics, the piano part in this ballad imitates the trotting rhythm of the pony — with all its attendant discomfort. One cannot help longing for the wretched animal to break into a canter or to start walking.

MY AIN FOLK

Words by
Wilfrid Mills

Music by
Laura G. Lemon

My Ain Folk

joy and sad-ness min-gle, As I list some auld-warld lay. And it's oh! but I'm

long-ing for my ain folk, Tho' they be but low-ly, puir, and plain folk: I am

far be-yond the sea, But my heart will ev-er be At hame in dear auld

Scot-land, wi' my ain folk! O' their ab-sent ain they're

tell-ing The auld folk by the fire: And I mark the swift tears well-ing, As the

77

A Garden Hard by Heaven

rud - dy flame leaps high'r How the mi - ther wad ca - ress me Were I but by her side: Now she

prays that Heav'n will bless me, Tho' the storm-y seas di - vide. And it's oh! but I'm

long-ing for my ain folk, Tho' they be but low-ly, puir, and plain folk: I am

far beyond the sea, But my heart will ev - er be At hame in dear auld Scot - land, wi' my

ain folk! A bon-nie lass is greeting, Tho' she strives to stay the

78

My Ain Folk

tears:— Ah! sweet will be our meet-ing Af-ter mon-y wea-ry years. Soon my fond arms shall en-

fold ye, As I ca' you ev-er mine__ Still a-bides the love I told ye In the

days of auld lang syne. And it's oh! but I'm long-ing for my ain folk, Tho' they be but

low-ly, puir, and plain folk: I am far a-cross the sea, But__ soon a-gain I'll

be At hame in dear auld Scot-land, wi' my ain folk!

MY AIN FOLK

1.   Far frae my hame I wander;
      But still my thoughts return
      To my ain folk ower yonder,
      In the sheiling by the burn.
      I see the cosy ingle,
      And the mist abune the brae:
      And joy and sadness mingle,
      As I list some auld-warld lay.

      And it's oh! but I'm longing for my ain folk,
      Tho' they be but lowly, puir, and plain folk:
      I am far beyond the sea,
      But my heart will ever be
      At hame in dear auld Scotland, wi' my ain folk!

2.   O' their absent ain they're telling -
      The auld folk by the fire:
      And I mark the swift tears welling,
      As the ruddy flame leaps high'r.
      How the mither wad caress me
      Were I but by her side:
      Now she prays that Heav'n will bless me,
      Tho' the stormy seas divide.

      And it's oh! but I'm longing for my ain folk, *etc.*

3.   A bonnie lass is greeting,
      Tho' she strives to stay the tears:
      Ah! sweet will be our meeting
      After mony weary years.
      Soon my fond arms shall enfold ye,
      As I ca' you ever mine -
      Still abides the love I told ye
      In the days of auld lang syne.

      And it's oh! but I'm longing for my ain folk, *etc.*

Whilst Irish songs, real and imitation, had an immense vogue throughout the Victorian and Edwardian periods, Scottish sounds were muted. This is something of a musical mystery, for there was no lack of raw material. There had been George Thomson who published between 1792 and 1841 no less than six volumes of Scottish tunes complete with 'select and characteristic verses by the most admired Scottish Poets' including Burns and Scott in settings by such impressive personalities as Haydn and Beethoven. Maybe Thomson lacked the charm, common touch and talent for show-business of his contemporary Thomas Moore, whose *Irish Melodies* started the Hibernian ballad industry. The worthy Thomson moved on to collect Welsh and Irish items, continuing to employ his prestigious composers, but he was probably too serious for success in the parlour. It was not as though Scotland was unfashionable either. The Prince Consort and the Prince of Wales donned the kilt and a piper marched outside the windows of Balmoral each morning the Queen was in residence, but even royal favour failed to introduce Scottish airs to the drawing-room in any numbers. The mellifluous Mendelssohn was on hand to represent Scotland to a wider audience, but he was mostly impressed by the fury of the Atlantic beating on Hebridean shores and his songs remained respectably Germanic. His Scottish Symphony did employ elements of Scottish folk-music but hardly in a way to excite a popular rush to the original melodies.

The lyricist and composer of 'My Ain Folk' seem to have escaped the reference books; this ballad appears to have been their one popular success. However, there were several musical Lemons active in the late nineteenth and early twentieth centuries: a song by one of them, Mary Mark Lemon, appears in the anthology, *Just a Song at Twilight* by the present editors. Mary Mark and Laura G. Lemon were probably two of the seven daughters of the famous co-founder of *Punch*, Mark Lemon (1809-70).

The simple strophic setting of this piece boasts almost every tear-jerking device in its musical line: the feminine endings to the lines and upward octave swoops almost dare singer and audience alike to swallow the rising lump in the throat. It is, incidentally, nearly impossible for the hearer not to join in the chorus. This is a real gem of a song.

GLORIOUS DEVON

Words by
Harold Boulton

Music by
Edward German

Glorious Devon

maid ens fair as the ap-ple bud, And her men are men in deed.

When sung with Chorus, repeat *ff*

When A-dam and Eve were dis-pos-ess'd Of the Gar-den hard by Hea-ven, They plant-ed an-oth-er one down in the West,_ 'Twas De-von,_ 'twas De-von glo-rious De-von. When von.

CHORUS

Spi-rits to old world

83

A Garden Hard by Heaven

he - roes wake, By ri - ver and cove and hoe,____ Gren - ville, Haw - kins

Ra - leigh and Drake And a thou - sand more we know; ____ To ev' - ry land the____

wide world o'er Some slips of the old stock roam,____ Leal friends in peace, dread

foes in war, With hearts still true____ to____ home____ Old

Eng - land's coun - ties by____ the sea From East to West are sev - en, But the

Glorious Devon

A Garden Hard by Heaven

cow,____ What 'ud Old En-gland with - out 'em do? And where 'ud 'un be___ to___

now?____ As crum - py as a lump___ of lead Be a

loaf without good lea - ven, And the yeast Mo-ther England do use for her bread____ Be

De - von,____ be De - von,__ glo - rious De - von, As

De - von,__ glo - rious De - von.

GLORIOUS DEVON

1.   Coombe and Tor, green meadow and lane,
   Birds on the waving bough,
   Beetling cliffs by the surging main,
   Rich red loam for the plough;
   Devon's the fount of the bravest blood
   That braces England's breed,
   Her maidens fair as the apple bud,
   And her men are men indeed.

   When Adam and Eve were dispossess'd
   Of the Garden hard by Heaven,
   They planted another one down in the West,
   'Twas Devon, 'twas Devon, glorious Devon.

2.   Spirits to old-world heroes wake,
   By river and cove and hoe,
   Grenville, Hawkins, Raleigh and Drake
   And a thousand more we know;
   To ev'ry land the wide world o'er
   Some slips of the old stock roam,
   Leal friends in peace, dread foes in war,
   With hearts still true to home.

   Old England's counties by the sea
   From East to West are seven,
   But the gem of that fair galaxy
   Is Devon, is Devon, glorious Devon.

3.   Dorset, Somerset, Cornwall, Wales,
   May envy the likes of we,
   For the flow'r of the West, the first, the best,
   The pick of the bunch us be;
   Squab pie, junket, and cyder brew,
   Richest of cream from the cow,
   What 'ud Old England without 'em do?
   And where 'ud 'un be to now?

   As crumpy as a lump of lead
   Be a loaf without good leaven,
   And the yeast Mother England do use for her bread
   Be Devon, be Devon, glorious Devon.

There had been drawing-room ballads celebrating the English countryside before the accession of King Edward, but it was during his reign that lyricists and composers discovered and joyously exploited the potential of apple blossom, shady lanes, sandy coves and rustic accents. Thus was born the mythical land of Mummerset, still an effective ally of the English Tourist Board.

Prominent among the influences producing this phenomenon was the nascent folk-song movement. Rude traditional airs had been prettied-up for polite audiences ever since the late eighteenth century, but a sterner academic interest in the reality behind the charming fancy dress was already evident by the late 1830s when William Chappell, founder of the Musical Antiquarian Society, was bringing out *English National Airs*, to be expanded into *The Popular Music of the Olden Times* which became a quarry of gems to be mined and polished by later composers. In the 'nineties the folk-song collectors were on the march *en masse*, some scrupulously recording, others revising the sexy and scatalogical which were such an inconvenient facet of the popular muse. Their publications proliferated, among them William Alexander Barrett's *English Folk Songs*, *Songs of the West* by the Reverend Sabine Baring-Gould (composer of 'Onward Christian Soldiers') and the Reverend H. Fleetwood Sheppard, Frank Kidson's *English Peasant Songs of the North Countrie* (note the self-conscious archaism) and J.A. Fuller-Maitland's *English County Songs*. In 1898 came the foundation of the Folk Song Society with a roll-call of famous members: musicians and composers, poets and antiquarians. Cecil Sharp was a leading purist; he alone collected some 3,000 songs. Inevitably there was some confusion about what was genuine, what bowdlerized for contemporary taste and what was imitation. Prejudices flourished: the truly rural was honest and organic whilst popular music composed for money was meretricious; the countryside was a sound, respectable source, industrial towns were somehow polluted and unworthy of notice — an interesting sentiment in accord with the socialism of William Morris. But whatever the doctrinal positions, composers and lyricists, both serious and commercial, were swift to descend like eager crows to pick the eyes out of the great body of newly-discovered songs: Sir Charles Stanford, Vaughan Williams, Percy Grainger, Edward German, Wilfrid Sanderson and Eric Coates all joined in the feast.

By grotesque irony, at the same time as the middle class was discovering the musical and literary delights of the countryside, the countryside itself was in the grip of creeping agricultural decay, a process that had started with the industrial revolution and reached disaster proportions in the 1870s. Even in the comfortable days of Edward, farm labourers in many parts of England were near to starvation in a bad year. The country people of Britain did not own the land; in this regard they were unique in Europe and, as Sir Charles Petrie has said, they 'found no attraction in the cheerless toil of an agricultural labourer upon what was a scanty wage. In consequence the villages increasingly tended to be left to old women and children, while the ancient skilled occupations were becoming lost arts'. By 1901 about 77 per cent of British people lived in towns.

As the countryside subsided into poverty and neglect, a compensating fantasy was born. Merrie England, as celebrated in jolly, comfortable songs in the suburban drawing-room and then on the London stage in Edward German's *Merrie England* and Lionel Monckton's *The Country Girl*, was nostalgia triumphant. Ronald Pearsall has called the style 'Olde-Englishe-tea-shoppe', for it was at its most meretricious the musical equivalent of the traditional Christmas card with its stage-coaches and (as Ogden Nash put it) 'hostlers hostling in an old inn yard'. And there was a clear link, too, with the patriotic idea; after all 'Drake he was a Devon man' and no doubt expressed his bellicosity in a quaint West Country burr.

'Glorious Devon' is the supreme example of its genre; it was also probably Edward German's most popular song. Oddly enough it attracted no particular attention on its publication as one of *Three Baritone Songs* until a professional singer unearthed it and gave it at a concert.

Sir Harold Boulton specialized in verses for songs of the countryside; his geographical spread was wide, from *Three Songs of the Heather* and *Songs of the North* to *Songs of Four Nations*, working with many different composers. As well as 'Glorious Devon' one other piece of his has achieved immortality, the 'Skye Boat Song'; it is still often mistaken for a genuine folk-song. Ever responsive to popular sentiment, in Edwardian times he turned his muse to the imperial theme, and Edward German set his patriotic hymn 'Canada'.

Sir Edward German (1862-1936) was born Edward German Jones in Shropshire. Whilst at the Royal Academy of Music he won a medal for a 'Te Deum' and his operetta *The Rival Poets* was staged. At the age of twenty-five he was director of music at the Globe Theatre and he composed a great deal of incidental music for Shakespearean productions. He also wrote symphonies and conducted at northern music festivals. Then came the famous series of comic operas, among them his completion of Sir Arthur Sullivan's unfinished *The Emerald Isle* (1901), *Merrie England* (1902), *The Princess of Kensington* (1903) and *Tom Jones* (1907). He was hailed as the successor to Sullivan, but despite the charm and freshness of his music, something was lacking: perhaps a librettist who was worthy of him.

The Edwardian song that everyone knows, 'Glorious Devon', owes everything to the robust melody. German has set the words flawlessly, and the result is an eminently singable song. It demonstrates to perfection the ballad composer's art that conceals art.

MY DEAR SOUL

Words by
May Byron

Music by
Wilfrid Sanderson

Hast thou heard the tur - tle dove, When the woods are green,

Sing - ing to his mate of love, All his heart may mean?____

So with words as sweet as birds Sof - ly I'd con - dole,

My Dear Soul

Sing for thee, sigh for thee, My dear soul!

Hast thou heard the rob - in red, In the yel - low
fall, Sing - ing, through the flow'rs be fled,
And the north winds call? So I'd come, when

91

A Garden Hard by Heaven

skies are glum, When the rains do roll, Cher-ish thee, com-fort thee, My dear soul! Hast thou heard the night-in-gale, In the sum-mer dark, Sing-ing down the si-lent vale, Ne'er a one to

My Dear Soul

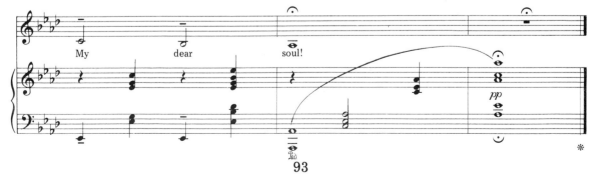

MY DEAR SOUL

1. Hast thou heard the turtle dove,
   When the woods are green,
   Singing to his mate of love,
   All his heart may mean?
   So with words as sweet as birds
   Softly I'd condole,
   Sing for thee, sigh for thee,
   My dear soul!

2. Hast thou heard the robin red,
   In the yellow fall,
   Singing, though the flow'rs be fled,
   And the north winds call?
   So I'd come, when skies are glum,
   When the rains do roll,
   Cherish thee, comfort thee,
   My dear soul!

3. Hast thou heard the nightingale,
   In the summer dark,
   Singing down the silent vale,
   Ne'er a one to hark?
   So I'd bide when from thy side
   Light and joy be stole,
   Live for thce, die for thee,
   My dear soul!

Here is a text for 'My Dear Soul' in good, rich Wessex dialect:

1. Hast thee heard the culver dove,
   When the woods be green,
   Zingen' to his mate o' love,
   All his heart do mean?
   Zo wi' words as sweet as birds
   I would softly tole,
   Zing vor 'ee, zigh for 'ee,
   My dear zoul!

2. Hast thee heard the robin rid,
   In the yaller fall,
   Zingen', tho' the flow'rs be hid,
   And the no'th winds call?
   Zo I'd come, when skies be glum
   When the rains do roll,
   Cherish 'ee, comfort 'ee,
   My dear zoul!

3. Hast thee heard the nightingale,
   In the zummer dark
   Zingen' down the zidelen vale,
   Ne'er a one to hark?
   Zo I'd bide, when from thi zide
   Light and joy be stole,
   Live for 'ee, die for 'ee,
   My dear zoul!

May Byron was one of many lyricists writing for various composers in the Edwardian period whose life and work has sunk into oblivion despite a mild reputation in her time. This is probably the only song of hers that would attract attention now; with its simple direct charm it marries very well with its setting. There are notes on the composer Wilfrid Sanderson on pages 61-2.

The setting itself will satisfy even the timid singer who may be daunted by the dialect words — although they do add enormously to the performance. The dying falls in the final bars of each verse are reminiscent of the same composer's setting of 'Friend o' Mine (see page 199). Sanderson's trick of making the same falls take an upward turn in the final verse is very telling.

THE CORNISH EMIGRANT'S SONG

Words by
Robert Stephen Hawker

Music by
James R. Dear

Quickly and with spirit

Oh! the east-ern winds are blow-ing; The breez-es seem to say, 'We are go-ing we are go-ing To North A-mer-i-cay.

There the mer-ry bees are hum-ming A-round a poor man's hive; Par-son King-don is not com-ing To take a-way the tithe. There the yel-low corn is grow-ing, Free as the King's high

97

A Garden Hard by Heaven

way; So, we're go ing, we are go - ing To

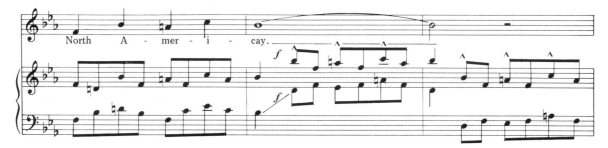

North A - mer - i - cay.

Un - cle Rab shall be church - war - den, And

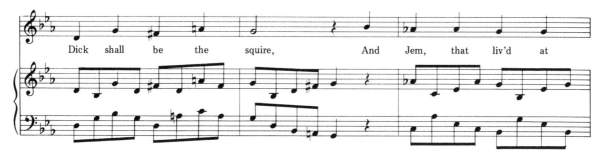

Dick shall be the squire, And Jem, that liv'd at

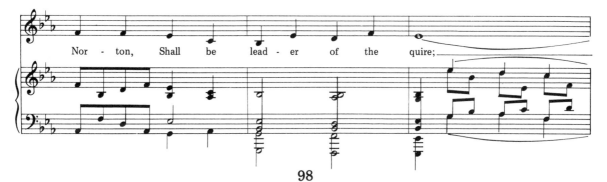

Nor - ton, Shall be lead - er of the quire;

THE CORNISH EMIGRANT'S SONG

1.   Oh! the eastern winds are blowing;
    The breezes seem to say,
    'We are going, we are going
    To North Americay.

2.   There the merry bees are humming
    Around a poor man's hive;
    Parson Kingdon is not coming
    To take away the tithe.

3.   There the yellow corn is growing
    Free as the King's highway;
    So, we're going, we are going
    To North Americay.

4.   Uncle Rab shall be churchwarden,
    And Dick shall be the squire,
    And Jem, that liv'd at Norton,
    Shall be leader of the quire;

5.   And I will be the preacher,
    And preach three times a day
    To ev'ry living creature
    In North Americay.'

Here is a Cornish lyric by a Cornish parson, although it must be admitted that he was born in Devon. The Reverend Robert Stephen Hawker (1803-75) is now chiefly celebrated for his stirring 'Song of the Western Men' ('And shall Trelawney die?/Here's twenty thousand Cornishmen/Will know the reason why!'), but he wrote a good deal of poetry, much of it in mock-medieval style. He had another, more curious distinction in that at the age of nineteen he married a widow of forty-one, but even this prudent action did not save him from perennial money problems. He was immortalized in Sabine Baring-Gould's book *Vicar of Morwenstow*.

So far, the editors of this book have failed to trace the identity of the composer, James R. Dear, or the existence of any other songs of his. He has added an unmistakable nautical flavour to Hawker's poetry in this simple strophic setting. It is an utterly convincing song with a very catchy tune that demands to be bellowed.

Dame Clara Butt

Dame Nellie Melba

Ada Crossley

Madame Antoinette Sterling

Four supreme exponents of the ballad

MACUSHLA

Words by
Josephine V. Rowe

Music by
Dermot MacMurrough

Macushla

feel their en - fold - ing ca - ress - ing me still. Fling them out of the dark - ness, my

lost love, Ma-cush - la, Let them find me and bind me a - gain if they will.

Ma - cush - la! Ma-cush - la! your red lips are say - ing That death is a dream, and

love is for aye. Then a - wa - ken, Macush - la, a wake from your dreaming, My blue-eyed Macush - la, a -

wa - ken to stay.

MACUSHLA

1. Macushla! Macushla! your sweet voice is calling,
   Calling me softly again and again.
   Macushla! Macushla! I hear its dear pleading,
   My blue-eyed Macushla, I hear it in vain.

2. Macushla! Macushla! your white arms are reaching,
   I feel their enfolding caressing me still.
   Fling them out from the darkness, my lost love, Macushla,
   Let them find me and bind me again if they will.

3. Macushla! Macushla! your red lips are saying
   That death is a dream, and love is for aye.
   Then awaken, Macushla, awake from your dreaming,
   My blue-eyed Macushla, awaken to stay.

From time to time, an unknown poet and an unknown composer combine to produce a hugely popular song and are never able to repeat their success. 'Macushla' is a good example: Josephine V. Rowe and Dermot MacMurrough, the begetters of this swooning piece of ballad Irishry, have disappeared into obscurity. The editors of this collection have found no traces of them, beyond their names.

Typical of the short song that follows the pattern of the larger three-decker ballad form, 'Macushla' displays the indefinable Hibernian touch that made it a perfect vehicle for John McCormack's voice. He made his famous recording of this song in March 1911, only a few months after it first appeared in print. It remains one of his best-loved performances.

LINDEN LEA

Words by
W. Barnes

Music by
R. Vaughan Williams

Within the wood-lands, flow'r-y glad-ed, By the oak trees' moss-y moot, The shin-ing grass blades, tim-ber sha-ded, Now do qui-ver un-der foot; And birds do whis-tle o-ver-head, And wa-ter's bub-bling in its bed; And there for

A Garden Hard by Heaven

me, The ap - ple tree Do lean down low in Lin - den Lea.

colla voce *mp*

mf

When leaves, that late - ly were a - spring - ing, Now do fade with - in the

rit.

copse, And paint - ed birds do hush their sing - ing, Up up - on the tim - ber

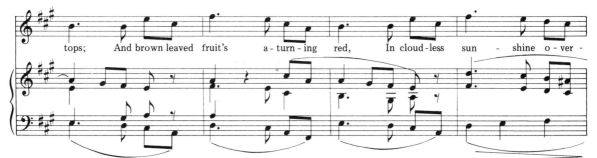

tops; And brown leaved fruit's a - turn - ing red, In cloud - less sun - shine o - ver -

- head, With fruit for me, The ap - ple tree Do lean down low in Lin - den

colla voce

Linden Lea

LINDEN LEA

1. Within the woodlands, flow'ry gladed,
    By the oak trees' mossy moot,
    The shining grass blades, timber shaded,
    Now do quiver under foot;
    And birds do whistle overhead,
    And water's bubbling in its bed;
    And there for me,
    The apple tree
    Do lean down low in Linden Lea.

2. When leaves, that lately were a-springing,
    Now do fade within the copse,
    And painted birds do hush their singing,
    Up upon the timber tops;
    And brown leaved fruit's a-turning red,
    In cloudless sunshine overhead,
    With fruit for me,
    The apple tree
    Do lean down low in Linden Lea.

3. Let other folk make money faster,
    In the air of dark-room'd towns:
    I don't dread a peevish master,
    Though no man may heed my frowns.
    I be free to go abroad,
    Or take again my homeward road,
    To where, for me,
    The apple tree
    Do lean down low in Linden Lea.

The original text of 'Linden Lea' was in Dorset dialect. Here it is:

1. 'Ithin the woodlands, flow'ry glëaded,
    By the woak trees' mossy moot,
    The sheenen grass blëades timber shëaded,
    Now do quiver under voot;
    An' birds do whissle auverhead,
    An' water's bubblen in its bed;
    An' there vor me,
    The apple tree
    Do lean down low in Linden Lea.

2. When leaves, that leately were a-springen,
   Now do fade 'ithin the copse,
   An' painted birds do hush their zingen',
   Up upon the timber tops;
   An' brown leaved fruit's a-turning red,
   In cloudless zunsheen auverhead,
   Wi' fruit vor me,
   The apple tree
   Do lean down low in Linden Lea.

3. Let other vo'k mëake money vaster,
   In the air o' dark-room'd towns;
   I don't dread a peevish mëaster,
   Though noo man may heed my frowns.
   I be free to go abrode,
   Or take agëan my hwomeward road,
   To where, vor me,
   The apple tree
   Do lean down low in Linden Lea.

This wonderful song is one of the more impressive products of the folk-song revival: a warm-hearted evocation of the countryside that shows up the cheapness of the majority of contemporary rusticities. Even the mock Dorset dialect does not grate on the ear in this setting. Doctor Ralph Vaughan Williams (1872-1958) was the son of a Gloucestershire parson, and despite studies at the Royal College of Music under such masters as Parry and Stanford he was something of a late developer musically; whilst he was at Trinity College, Cambridge, his cousins averred that he was wasting his time in having ambitions as a composer. 'Linden Lea' was his earliest published work, dating from 1902, and a deep immersion in folk-song came shortly afterwards when he began to collect in the field, taking down hundreds of songs from country people in East Anglia and Herefordshire. His passion was sustained; late in life he became president of the English Folk Dance and Song Society. Most of his major works date from after the Edwardian period, but through them all runs the influence of folk-song and English choral music. He remained faithful too to vocal music; his final work was *Four Last Songs* of the year of his death.

Some of his contemporaries were somewhat underwhelmed by Vaughan Williams's preoccupation with folk-music and its incorporation into his work. One critic regretted that all the good doctor's music reminded him irresistibly of 'a cow looking over a gate'. However, in 'Linden Lea', where a rustic atmosphere would have been appropriate for Barnes's words, the composer produced instead a smooth and sophisticated melody that is as firmly diatonic as any contemporary Edwardian ballad.

If Vaughan Williams was to achieve international celebrity, his poet, W. Barnes, seems to have languished in obscurity and the editors have been unable to trace other works by him.

DANNY BOY

Words by
Fred E. Weatherly

Old Irish Air

Danny Boy

A Garden Hard by Heaven

ly - ing, And kneel and say an A - ve there for me; And I shall hear, though soft you tread a - bove me, And all my grave will warm - er, sweet - er be, For you will bend and tell me that you love me, And I shall sleep in peace un - til you come to me!

DANNY BOY

1.   Oh, Danny Boy, the pipes, the pipes are calling
    From glen to glen, and down the mountain side.
    The summer's gone and all the roses falling,
    It's you, it's you must go and I must bide.
    But come ye back when summer's in the meadow,
    Or when the valley's hushed and white with snow,
    It's I'll be here in sunshine or in shadow,
    Oh, Danny Boy, oh, Danny Boy, I love you so!

2.   But when ye come, and all the flowers are dying,
    If I am dead, as dead I well may be,
    Ye'll come and find the place where I am lying,
    And kneel and say an Ave there for me.
    And I shall hear, though soft you tread above me,
    And all my grave will warmer, sweeter be,
    For you will bend and tell me that you love me,
    And I shall sleep in peace until you come to me!

The tune of 'Danny Boy' is of course 'The Londonderry Air', and the story of the ballad is an interesting example of how a genuine folk-air could attract the tender attentions of more than one exploiter. For some unknown reason Thomas Moore of the *Irish Melodies* had never put words to the melody, although he must have known it. It appeared in a collection of ancient music in 1855, and more than half a century later the lyricist Fred E. Weatherly was sent a manuscript copy by a sister-in-law in America. As he knew of no other verses attached to the tune, he put words to it — an altered version of a song called 'Danny Boy' that he had already written a couple of years previously in 1910. The publisher Boosey accepted the song for publication and it then came to light that an old friend of Weatherly's, Alfred Perceval Graves, author of 'Trottin' to the Fair' which also appears in this volume, had already written two lyrics to the melody. Graves took strong exception to having the folk-tune 'poached', and it seems that the friendship with Weatherly came to an abrupt end.

The most prolific poet of the Edwardian — and for that matter Victorian and Georgian — ballad, the genial and indefatigable Fred E. (Frederick Edward) Weatherly (1848-1929) was virtually a one-man song factory. Seven of his lyrics appear in this book, but he wrote thousands, of which at least fifteen hundred were published, with music by dozens of composers who vied to get their hands on his verses. As early as 1879 *Musical Jottings* remarked about a song by (Sir) Frederic Cowen: 'The poetry is by F.E. Weatherly, who seems the only poet the first composers care to notice just now.' One of thirteen children of a Somerset doctor, he was educated at Hereford Cathedral School and about this time he sent his first schoolgirl love a book of Byron's poems only to have it swiftly returned by a teacher as being 'a gift not suitable for you to give or for her to receive'. Oxford followed, and for twenty years he worked as a crammer for dull boys. The law was as much a love as poetry, and he studied and was called to the Bar at the age of thirty-nine, thereafter enjoying a comfortable career on the Western Circuit, often appearing in criminal cases, almost invariably for the defence. According to his own account, in court he was remarkably keen-witted and effective. Songs poured from him, he translated opera (including *Cav.* and *Pag.*) and he published quantities of verse and children's books. He revelled in his considerable celebrity. A little man physically, he had, as a friend put it, 'a blithe and tender soul'. He may have been self-satisfied but he was much loved and was certainly no fool, cheerfully dismissing his facility as a lyricist as no safe ticket to Parnassus. His most commercially successful ballad was 'Roses of Picardy' which became one of the great popular songs of the Great War, and it made its writer a small fortune.

'Laurence Hope'

Sir Harold Boulton

Fred E. Weatherly

Three lyricists

UP FROM SOMERSET

Words by
Fred E. Weatherly

Music by
Wilfrid Sanderson

Oh, we came up from Som-er-set, To see the Great Re-view; There was Ma-ry drest in her Sun-day best, And our boy Bil-lee too, The drums were roll-ing rub-a-dub, The trum-pets toot-led

Up from Somerset

too, When right up rode His Ma-jes-ty, An' says 'An' who be you?' _____ 'Oh, we'm come up from Som-er-set, Where the ci-der ap-ples grow, We'm come to see your Ma-jes-ty, An' how the world do go. And when you're want-ing an-y-one, If you'll kind-ly let us know, We'll all come up from Som-er-set, Be-cause we loves you

so!'

Then the Queen she look'd at Ma - ry, 'An' what's your name?'_ she _

said, But Ma - ry blush'd like an - y rose, An' hung her pret - ty

head. So I ups and nud - ges Ma - ry, 'Speak up, and tell her,

do!' So she said 'If you please, your Ma - jes - ty, My name is Ma - ry

Up from Somerset

too! _____ An' we'm come up from Som-er-set, Where the

ci – der ap – ples grow, Where the gals can hem an' sew an' stitch, And

al – so reap ___ and hoe, An' if you're want – ing an – y gals, An' will

kind – ly let us know, We'll all come up from Som-er-set, Be –

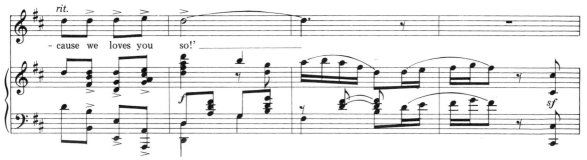

– cause we loves you so!' _____

A Garden Hard by Heaven

Then the King look'd down at Bil-lee-boy, Be-fore they rode_ a-way, 'An' what is he go-ing for to be?' His Ma-jes-ty did say. So Bil-lee pull'd his fore-lock, An' stood up trim_ and true, 'Oh, I'm goin' to be a sol-dier, Sir,_ For I wants to fight for you!'

Up from Somerset

For we'm come up from Som-er-set, Where the ci-der ap-ples

grow, For we're all King's men in Som-er-set, As they were long, long a-

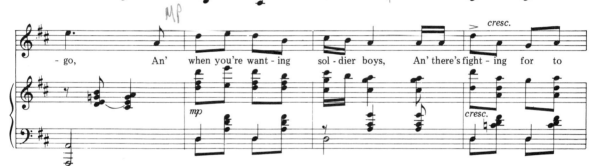

-go, An' when you're want-ing sol-dier boys, An' there's fight-ing for to

do, You just send word to Som-er-set, An' we'll all be up for

you!"

121

UP FROM SOMERSET

1.   Oh, we came up from Somerset,
To see the Great Review;
There was Mary drest in her Sunday best,
And our boy Billee too.
The drums were rolling rub-a-dub,
The trumpets tootled too,
When right up rode His Majesty,
An' says 'An who be you?'

'Oh, we'm come up from Somerset,
Where the cider apples grow,
We'm come to see your Majesty,
An' how the world do go.
And when you're wanting anyone,
If you'll kindly let us know,
We'll all come up from Somerset,
Because we loves you so!'

2.   Then the Queen she look'd at Mary,
'An' what's your name?' she said,
But Mary blush'd like any rose,
An' hung her pretty head.
So I ups and nudges Mary,
'Speak up and tell her, do!'
So she said 'If it please, your Majesty,
My name is Mary too!

An' we'm come up from Somerset,
Where the cider apples grow,
Where the gals can hem an' sew an' stitch,
And also reap and hoe,
An' if you're wanting any gals,
An' will kindly let us know,
We'll all come from Somerset,
Because we loves you so!'

3.   Then the King look'd down at Billee-boy,
Before they rode away,
'An' what is he going for to be?'
His Majesty did say.
So Billee pull'd his forelock,
And stood up trim and true,
'Oh, I'm going to be a soldier, Sir,
For I wants to fight for you!

For we'm come up from Somerset,
Where the cider apples grow,
For we're all King's men in Somerset,
As they were long, long ago,
An' when you're wanting soldier boys,
An' there's fighting for to do,
You just send word to Somerset,
An' we'll all be up for you!'

Launched successfully by the singer Ivor Foster in 1913, 'Up from Somerset' became really popular at the beginning of the Great War, perhaps because of the coy nostalgia and the fashionable note of simple patriotism in the third stanza. Sadly, many volunteer Billie-boys were to find a grave in the trampled mud of no-man's-land rather than in a blossom-strewn Somerset churchyard. The story of this ballad may seem a product of the song-writer's fantasy world, but Fred E. Weatherly said he wrote it out of intimate knowledge of his home county — he was born in Portishead — and could 'point out the sort of people who would have done and said what the father and mother and boy did and said at "The Great Review".' There is a note on Weatherly on pages 113-14 and on Wilfrid Sanderson on pages 61-2.

The composer's indication to join the opening notes of the chorus by portamento gives a clue to the ideal performance of this song, which should be unashamedly bucolic and perhaps not too accurate. This is, above all, a piece to be enjoyed and still appears, seventy years after its composition, to have a full glass in its hand. Maybe that is why it has been used so successfully by a firm of cider manufacturers as an advertising jingle.

3

Pale Hands I Loved

or, Songs of Passion

NIRVANA

Words by
Fred E. Weatherly

Music by
Stephen Adams

I have come from the si - lent for - est, My beau - ti - ful Lo - tos flow'r, And I stand in thy gar - den sigh - ing, It is the lov - ers' hour. Thy

Pale Hands I Loved

126

love.

I have knelt in the migh - ty tem - ples,

But the dumb gods make no sign;

They can-not speak to my spi - rit,

As thy soul speaks to mine.

And the priests talk of Nir - va - na,

And

127

Pale Hands I Loved

weave their mys - tic charms, _____

I on - ly know Nir - va - na With -

- in thy ___ lov - ing ___ arms ___

I on - ly know Nir - va - na With - in thy lov - ing

arms, thy lov - ing arms. And the

128

Nirvana

129

Pale Hands I Loved

NIRVANA

1. I have come from the silent forest,
   My beautiful Lotos flow'r,
   And I stand in thy garden sighing,
   It is the lovers' hour.
   Thy sisters, the lotos blossoms,
   They ope' to the moon above;
   Open thy window, beloved,
   And let me tell my love.

2. I have knelt in the mighty temples,
   But the dumb gods make no sign;
   They cannot speak to my spirit,
   As thy soul speaks to mine.
   And the priests talk of Nirvana,
   And weave their mystic charms,
   I only know Nirvana
   Within thy loving arms.

3. And the lotos flow'r will perish,
   The stars turn cold and grey,
   The dumb gods will be shattered,
   The temples old decay:
   But we shall be one, beloved,
   In the stream of life divine;
   As the river flows to the ocean,
   My soul shall flow to thine!

Stephen Adams was the *nom de plume* of the baritone Michael Maybrick (1844-1913). Born in Liverpool, he became a church organist at the age of fourteen and was fortunate enough to be a pupil of the great exponent of the organ and composer, W.T. Best. He went on to study in Leipzig and realized that he had more potential as a singer than as an organist. Maybrick was a regular performer at ballad concerts and a composer of a large number of songs in varied styles, one enormous success being 'The Blue Alsatian Mountains' which was a particular favourite in America. His compositions are particularly comfortable for the vocalist, not surprisingly, and he achieved a considerable rapport with Fred E. Weatherly for whom he made many happy settings, among them 'Nancy Lee', 'The Midshipmite' and 'The Holy City'. The rather sad story about the song he never composed for Weatherly, 'Friend o' Mine', appears on page 203. Notes on Weatherly are to be found on pages 113-14.

Apart from a few bars of what sounds suspiciously like 'Hollywood Red Indian' which do duty as a ritornello, 'Nirvana' is musically a companion piece for the same composer's 'Thora', which also appears in this volume. Both explore the possibilities of the sustained vocal line emerging from a running arpeggiated accompaniment — and very effective it is, too. 'Nirvana' is, it must be admitted, innocent of Eastern promise: it is just a jolly good 'sing'.

KASHMIRI SONG

Words by
Laurence Hope

Music by
Amy Woodforde-Finden

Moderato assai, con molto sentimento

Pale hand I loved be- side the Sha-li mar, ____ Where are you now? Who lies be - neath your spell? Whom do you lead on Rap-ture's road - way, far, ____ Be - fore you a - go-

Kashmiri Song

133

Pale Hands I Loved

I would have ra - ther felt you round my throat

Crush-ing out life, than wa - ving me fare - well! Crush-ing out life, than

wav - ing me fare - well Pale hands I loved be -

- side the Sha - li - mar, Where are you now? Where are you

now!

134

KASHMIRI SONG

1.   Pale hands I loved beside the Shalimar,
   Where are you now? Who lies beneath your spell?
   Whom do you lead on Rapture's roadway, far,
   Before you agonize them in farewell?
   Pale hands I loved beside the Shalimar,
   Where are you now? Where are you now?

2.   Pale hands, pinked tipped, like Lotus buds that float
   On those cool waters where we used to dwell,
   I would have rather felt you round my throat
   Crushing out life, than waving me farewell!
   Pale hands I loved beside the Shalimar,
   Where are you now? Where are you now?

The story told by the lyric of this archetypal Edwardian ballad was rumoured to be true: the love of the son of a Kashmiri rajah for a married English lady. The story behind the lyric is equally exotic and definitely true. The *Four Indian Love Lyrics* of which 'Kashmiri Song' is one — the others being 'The Temple Bells are Ringing', 'Till I Wake' (see page 137) and 'Less than the Dust' — first appeared in a collection of verse by 'a new and refreshingly virile poet', as the *St James's Gazette* put it. In fact the masculine bard, Laurence Hope, was the wife of a Bengal Army officer, and the passion of her verse was not entirely novel, however inconsistent it may seem now with the popular idea of the tastes of middle-class society whether in England or in India. Actually, it was in a well-established tradition. The American poetess Ella Wheeler Wilcox had already stimulated a palpitating following with such uninhibited demands as 'Here is my body, bruise it if you will', as early as 1876, and many a sheltered British maiden had been deliciously excited by the whirling words of Algernon Swinburne.

'Laurence Hope' was born Adela Florence Cory (1865-1904) in Gloucestershire in the same year as Rudyard Kipling, the daughter of an officer in the Indian Army who edited the *Sind Gazette*. Her sister also had a literary bent and was to become the novelist, Victoria Cross. Adela joined her parents in Karachi at the age of sixteen and, again like Kipling, worked on her father's newspaper. Soon she fell under the spell, not of the expected polo-playing subaltern, but of Mother India, and then in 1889 she met the romantic and handsome Colonel Malcolm Nicolson, over twenty years her senior and already legendary for such exploits as crossing the Mango Pir River hopping from the back of one crocodile to another. He took her by storm; they married and five years of high adventure followed. On the Zhob Valley expedition of 1890 she followed her beloved through the wild and dangerous passes of the Afghan border disguised as a Pathan boy. She began to write poetry with an unbridled, erotic quality, albeit with an occasional touch of bathos:

My hands, my lips are feverish with the longing and the waiting
And no softness of the twilight soothes their heat,
Till I see your radiant eyes, shining stars beneath the starlight
Till I kiss the slender coolness of your feet.

Such fervour was soon to find an echo in the novels of Elinor Glyn.

Published in 1902, Laurence Hope's *The Garden of Kama* was an instant success, and the musical settings of the *Four Indian Love Lyrics* by the wife of another Indian Army officer conferred immortality upon them.

No wonder, for they were in the mainstream of contemporary outpourings about the never-never-land of the East. Among the artistes who took up the songs was Dame Clara Butt, whose formidable physique often seemed at odds with the delicacy of some of the sentiments she was called upon to express. But the story of Laurence Hope was drawing to a close. After the acclaim of London society she and her husband, now a general, left their baby with relatives and returned to India, unable to live anywhere else. Whilst undergoing an unromantic prostate operation in Madras, Nicolson died under the anaesthetic. Heartbroken, his wife arranged for the publication of her last book of poems and two months after her husband's death committed suicide. The passionate couple lie together in St Mary's Cemetery in Madras.

The story of the publication of the *Four Indian Love Lyrics* and a brief biography and appreciation of the composer Amy Woodforde-Finden appear on page 140.

Of the four famous *Lyrics*, the 'Kashmiri Song' was the most popular: it was even recorded, excruciatingly badly, by Rudolph Valentino who inevitably found it too difficult to get quite right. The oriental pentatonic introduction, now something of a cliché, still manages to sound convincing in a sensitive interpretation, and the long rolling phrases thrown backwards and forwards between singer and pianist really do suggest the heat and vast spaces of India. Throughout the song the pianist supports the vocal line without ever intruding on its intensity. Finally the accompaniment dies away in three masterly bars that echo the opening phrases. Performers of the 'Kashmiri Song' should follow the composer's directions minutely: they will find they are exhaustive, unambiguous and essential to a perfect rendering.

TILL I WAKE

Words by
Laurence Hope

Music by
Amy Woodforde-Finden

Pale Hands I Loved

139

TILL I WAKE

When I am dying, lean over me tenderly, softly, --
Stoop, as the yellow roses droop
In the wind from the South;
So I may when I wake, if there be an awakening,
Keep, what lulled me to sleep,
The touch of your lips on my mouth.

With hindsight, the qualities of the *Four Indian Love Lyrics* may be obvious enough, but when Amy Woodforde-Finden sent them on the round of publishers including Boosey & Co. they were turned down. After about a year she published them herself, and it was a recommendation to the singer Hamilton Earle that started them on their career. He sang them in the provinces and so well were they received that Earle spoke to Arthur Boosey, and after a while the latter agreed to publish them. Success was then instantaneous.

A great ballad is made when fine words and fine music meet and merge. In these songs that miracle occurred. Additionally fascinating were the facts that the author and composer did not meet until the poems had acquired their musical settings, and that they were both such remarkable figures — neither of them a repressed English lady with a talent for parlour music. If 'Laurence Hope' had the more adventurous life, that of the composer was hardly uneventful.

Amy Woodforde-Finden (1860-1919) was born Amelia Ward, the daughter of an American citizen who happened to be British Consul in Valparaiso, Chile. She was one of nine children, four of whom did not survive, and when her father died her mother swept the family off to South Kensington and they were all naturalized as English. Little Amy later described herself as something of a child prodigy, composing a song at the age of nine and a waltz, subsequently published, at fifteen. She studied the piano and wrote a few songs under the name of Amy Ward. They attracted little attention until after she became famous; only one is occasionally heard today, 'O Flower of All the World'. For three years she lived in India, travelling in Kashmir and marrying a lieutenant-colonel, a medical officer in the Bengal Cavalry who had served with Colonel Nicolson, the husband of 'Laurence Hope'. It was on her return to England after her marriage that she set four poems from *The Garden of Kama*, just published and a popular sensation. She wrote to the publishers to ask permission to put them to music; in return she had a cable from Morocco: 'Yes, with pleasure. No fee. Laurence Hope.' The *Lyrics* made Amy's name, and she went on to write many more song cycles, some of them drawing on the Latin American world of her childhood, others capitalizing on the exoticism of the East that had proved so fruitful for her. Surviving her husband by three years, she died — still composing — at the piano in her London flat and was buried at Hampsthwaite, Yorkshire, where her memorial, a recumbent figure in white marble, is something to behold.

As a composer, Amy Woodforde-Finden was something of a mina bird, metaphorically speaking. She seems to have been able to slip into a sari or kimono as the subject required and to draw on a great wealth of half-remembered musical phrases to suit the particular poetry she was setting. Of all her song sets and cycles, however, it was only the *Four Indian Love Lyrics* that achieved lasting fame, and justifiably for they are small master-pieces. The *Radio Times* said in the 'twenties: 'If sales are any criterion of popularity, the most popular songs ever published in the history of music are the *Indian Love Lyrics*. . . . it will suffice to keep her memory green as long as there is a music-lover left to sing her songs or a band to play them.'

If the 'Kashmiri Song' became her most celebrated ballad, 'Till I Wake' is arguably the finest. It is an astonishing revelation in performance and bears comparison with the best romantic songs of any of the established com-posers. From the three knocks of fate in the introduction and the long leisurely phrases of the first verse to the whirlwind piano interlude and marcato bass of the closing bars, the song is a *tour de force* and takes Laurence Hope's verse out of the drawing-room into a far greater sphere.

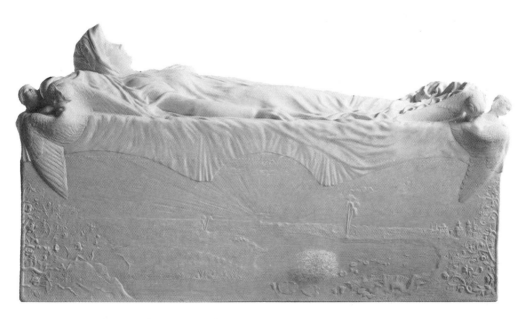

The tomb of Amy Woodforde-Finden

DREAMING OF THEE

Words by
Edgar Wallace

Music by
Augustus W. Barratt

Dreaming of Thee

left the world be - neath me love, my soul has tak - en wing To a
dream land where no sea - son is but thee.
Dream - ing of thee! dream - ing of thee! O
god - ly gift that brings you back to me. I
tread the fair - y bridge that spans the gulf of time and space, I

Pale Hands I Loved

close my eyes and rend the veil that hides you from my face, And
lo! my lit - tle dark - ling world be comes a won - drous place, My___
lit - tle world is glor - i - fied by thee!
Dream-ing of thee! dream - ing of thee! Tho' fraught with pain the wak-ing hour___
be, Tho' chill and low - er - ing the dawn that

144

Dreaming of Thee

meets my open-ing eyes, Tho' drear and emp-ty be the task that

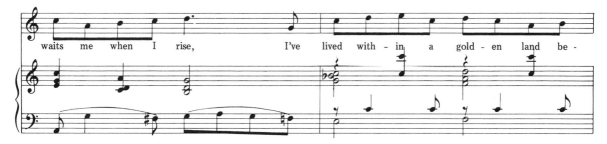

waits me when I rise, I've lived with-in a gold-en land be-

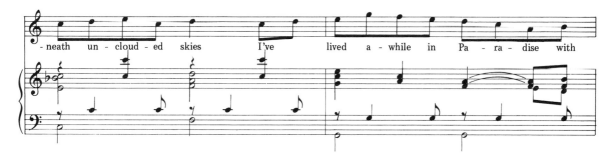

-neath un-cloud-ed skies I've lived a-while in Pa-ra-dise with

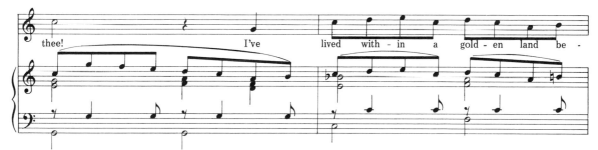

thee! I've lived with-in a gold-en land be-

-neath un-cloud-ed skies, I've lived a-while in Pa-ra-dise with thee!

DREAMING OF THEE

1.   Dreaming of thee! dreaming of thee!
   The world's a barren wilderness for me.
   Perchance it may be summertime, mayhap it is but spring,
   Perchance the bees go flowerward, perchance the robins sing;
   I've left the world beneath me, love, my soul has taken wing
   To a dreamland where no season is but thee.

2.   Dreaming of thee! dreaming of thee!
   O godly gift that brings you back to me.
   I tread the fairy bridge that spans the gulf of time and space,
   I close my eyes and rend the veil that hides you from my face,
   And lo! my little darkling world becomes a wondrous place,
   My little world is glorified by thee!

3.   Dreaming of thee! dreaming of thee!
   Tho' fraught with pain the waking hour be,
   Tho' chill and lowering the dawn that meets my opening eyes,
   Tho' drear and empty be the task that waits me when I rise,
   I've lived within a golden land beneath unclouded skies,
   I've lived awhile in Paradise with thee!

Probably the title of this ballad is now best known from the parody version 'Dreaming of Thee', one of the *Odd Odes* of the English comedian, Cyril Fletcher. The rumti-tum rhythm of the original certainly invites such treatment, but in its time the song had a considerable vogue. It began life on the stage, in the musical sketch, *The M.I.s* (Mounted Infantry).

Nowadays Edgar Wallace (1872-1932) is scarcely remembered as anything other than the phenomenal author of about a hundred and fifty thrillers, which he called 'pirate stories in modern dress', beginning with *The Four Just Men* of 1905. In the first ten years of the century, however, he was chiefly celebrated as a war correspondent and a poet in a kind of reach-me-down Kiplingesque style. His life-story was a classic of the rags-to-riches genre. A penniless orphan, he was saved from the workhouse by a fish porter who sent him to school in Peckham in South London. Wallace's early jobs included working in a rubber factory, on a Grimsby trawler and (of course) as a newspaper seller. He joined the Army and served in the Boer War of 1899-1902, returning to South Africa as a newspaperman and correspondent for Reuters, incidentally writing a good deal of verse about the lot of Tommy Atkins. Back in England he published *The Four Just Men* himself and discovered his crock of gold. From then on with enormous gusto he devoted himself to adventure and crime stories, sometimes dictating them to turn them out the faster. Among them were *Sanders of the River*, *The Fellowship of the Frog* and *The Squeaker*. Some tales he dramatized with great success, among them his horse-racing melodramas. Wallace not only knew what the public wanted; he created his personal production line to supply it.

Dreaming of Thee

Augustus Barratt wrote a number of songs, 'My Ships' among them, but with 'Dreaming of Thee' he seems to have touched his apogee, such as it was. Typical of the short strophic songs that won enormous popularity at the beginning of the century, this ballad is direct and effective in performance. One cannot help but wish, nonetheless, that the poet had been able to improve on 'perchance the bees go flowerward'.

'Stephen Adams'   Wilfrid Sanderson

Henri Trotère   Edward German

Four 'popular' ballad composers

ROSES

Words by
Fred E. Weatherly

Music by
Stephen Adams

I send thee red, red ro - ses, To tell __ thee of the morn, When first a - mong the ro - ses Our hap - py love was born, Our hap - py love was born. I

Pale Hands I Loved

Roses

Pale Hands I Loved

ROSES

1. I send thee red, red roses,
To tell thee of the morn,
When first among the roses
Our happy love was born.
I send thee white, white roses,
To tell thee of the night,
The night in all its beauty,
With all its dreams and light.

2. And when thou seest the roses,
This will the roses say,
There is no day without thee,
No night when thou'rt away;
No day I do not love thee,
No night I do not pray
That God will bless and guard thee,
For ever, night and day!

This is the passionate song that set John McCormack on the road to acclaim in fashionable London society. Perceval Graves (see page 75) reported how his friend, the young Irish tenor, was heard singing 'Roses' by the elderly Duchess of Devonshire, hearing-trumpet to her ear. McCormack 'gave out a ringing A natural with tremendous conviction. This with the other numbers, no doubt from his Irish repertory, did the trick. The old lady was so delighted that she told all her friends and acquaintances about the young minstrel, who soon became swamped with lucrative engagements'.

A glance at any index of ballads shows a remarkable representation of the family *Rosaceae*; prominent are such items as 'Roses', 'The Rose', 'My Rose', 'I Sent You Roses', 'Rose in the Bud', 'The Rose of Erin', 'The Life of a Rose', 'The Rose on My Life', 'Rose of the World', 'A Land of Roses', 'In My Garden of Roses', 'Roses by Summer Forsaken', 'Mighty Lak a Rose' (also in this volume), 'Unmindful of the Roses' (as if anyone could be), 'Roses and Rue', 'Roses of Picardy', 'Go, Pretty Rose', 'The Bird and the Rose' and, inevitably, 'Roses All the Way'. The only word that seems to outnumber 'rose' in song titles is, of course, 'love'.

There are notes on the author and composer of this ballad on pages 113-14 and 131 respectively.

A simple strophic setting like many of Adams's songs, 'Roses' is better in performance than it looks on the page. Doubtless the composer, alias the singer Michael Maybrick, gave telling renditions of the piece himself. It is very much a 'singer's song'.

THORA

Words by
Fred E. Weatherly

Music by
Stephen Adams

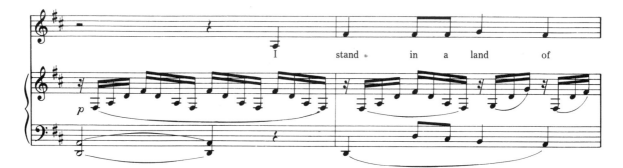

I stand in a land of

ro - ses, But I dream of a land of

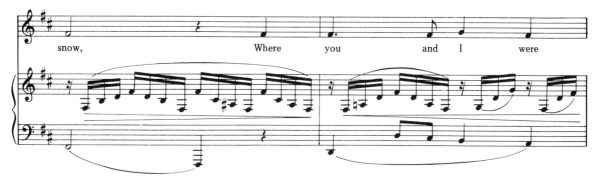

snow, Where you and I were

Thora

hap - py, In the years of long a -

-go. Night - in - gales in the

branch - es, Stars in the mag - ic

skies, But I on - ly hear you sing - ing, I

on - ly see your eyes, I on - ly hear you

Pale Hands I Loved

Thora

An - gel of love to me!

I

stand a - gain in the North land, But in si - lence and in

shame; Your grave is my on - ly land - mark, And

men have for - got - ten my name. 'Tis a tale that is tru - er and

Pale Hands I Loved

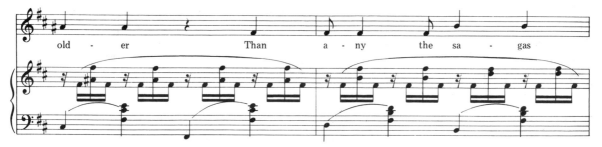

old - er Than a - ny the sa - gas

tell, I lov'd you in life too lit - tle, I

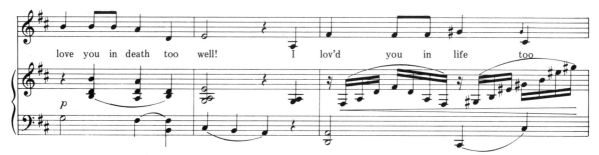

love you in death too well! I lov'd you in life too

lit - tle, I lov'd you in death too well.

Speak! speak! speak to me, Tho - ra, Speak from your Heav'n to

159

THORA

1.   I stand in a land of roses,
    But I dream of a land of snow,
    Where you and I were happy,
    In the years of long ago.
    Nightingales in the branches,
    Stars in the magic skies,
    But I only hear you singing,
    I only see your eyes.

    Come! come! come to me, Thora,
    Come once again and be
    Child of my dream, light of my life,
    Angel of love to me!

2.   I stand again in the North land,
    But in silence and in shame;
    Your grave is my only landmark,
    And men have forgotten my name.
    'Tis a tale that is truer and older
    Than any the sagas tell, -
    I lov'd you in life too little,
    I love you in death too well.

    Speak! speak! speak to me, Thora,
    Speak from your Heav'n to me;
    Child of my dream, love of my life,
    Hope of my world to be!

Fred E. Weatherly said that this ballad was 'of course' based on the novel by the fashionable Manx writer Hall Caine, and he hoped that it formed a fair summary of the story. Weatherly was particularly proud of the first two lines, and pointed out that 'I was always taught that the opening line or lines of a song should give the picture, and then if people will talk while the song is being sung at all events they know what the song is about'. Such a comment reminds one that in an Edwardian drawing-room ballads were not invariably listened to in respectful silence.

Another glimpse of the actuality of Edwardian taste is provided by Nancy Mitford's description in *The Pursuit of Love* of Uncle Matthew's latest passion, the 'new tune on his gramophone, called "Thora". "I live [sic] in a land of roses," boomed a deep male voice, "but dream of a land of snow. Speak, speak, SPEAK to me, Thora." He played it morning, noon and night.' Uncle Matthew, who was the simulacrum of the volcanic 'Farve' of the Mitford family, Lord Redesdale, was a definite product of an Edwardian upbringing, his musical tastes ranging from the records of Amelita Galli-Curci (until the traumatic day when he actually saw her in person) to 'Drake is going West, lad'.

Weatherly's life is summarized on pages 113-14 and Stephen Adams's on page 131.

One of the great warhorses of the Edwardian musical evening, 'Thora' is magnificent in performance. Singers need not be daunted by the slightly archaic Christian name of the dedicatee. If the song is sung with enough conviction even that hurdle will be overcome.

I HEAR YOU CALLING ME

Words by
Harold Harford

Music by
Charles Marshall

I Hear You Calling Me

kind stars' light. I hear you calling me. And oh, the ring-ing glad-ness of your voice! The words that made my long-ing heart re-joice You spoke, do you re-member? and my heart Still hears the dis-tant mu-sic of your voice. I hear you

163

Pale Hands I Loved

I HEAR YOU CALLING ME

1.   I hear you calling me.
   You called me when the moon had veiled her light,
   Before I went from you into the night;
   I came, do you remember? back to you
   For one last kiss beneath the kind stars' light.

2.   I hear you calling me.
   And oh, the ringing gladness of your voice!
   The words that made my longing heart rejoice
   You spoke, do you remember? and my heart
   Still hears the distant music of your voice.

3.   I hear you calling me.
   Though years have stretched their weary length between,
   And on your grave the mossy grass is green:
   I stand, do you behold me? listening here,
   Hearing your voice through all the years between.
   I hear you calling me.

One day, the lyricist Perceval Graves (see page 75) opened the door at his lodgings in Torrington Square in London, where he lived with a young tenor, John McCormack. On the doorstep stood Charles Marshall, 'who gave his name rather diffidently, with a request to meet McCormack who, luckily, happened to be at home, as he said: "I have a song here which I think will suit him." At that time Marshall was a struggling song-writer, a shade over fifty. Much encouraged by John's cordial reception, he sat down and played it over once and McCormack then began to sing it. After the first line, he became enthusiastic. "It's great. You must come with me at once to meet Mr Arthur Boosey. He is sure to take it." And he did.'

From then on, as Gordon T. Ledbetter says in his biography of the singer, 'throughout his career it remained to all intents and purposes the tenor's own property. Among his records, this song was far and away the best-seller'. In fact, McCormack recorded it many times and it is possible by following the changes in voice and presentation in the succession of discs to understand the extent of his development. The song is so closely identified with him that his wife Lily adopted it as the title of her biography of McCormack, *I Hear You Calling Me*, of 1950.

It is interesting to see, incidentally, how the great singer's career in its early stages was bound up with the ballad concerts promoted by Boosey & Co. His first major engagement in London was at one of them in 1907 in Queen's Hall. Francis Toye commented tersely upon the occasion: 'There was a new tenor called McCormack with lots of voice but no brains.'

Charles Marshall's 'I Hear You Calling Me' was his one great achievement but he also wrote another fairly popular gem, 'When Shadows Gather'. He had a musical namesake, Charles Marshall, an American tenor noted for heroic roles in Italian and French opera.

This is an inspired setting: the way in which Marshall sets the title words of the song allows us to imagine we can actually hear someone calling out. An intelligent performance can raise this simple ballad to the ranks of the really great songs of any period.

4

It's Home I Want to Be

or, Songs of Sentiment

MIGHTY LAK A ROSE

Words by
Frank L. Stanton

Music by
Ethelbert Nevin

Mighty Lak a Rose

Look-in' thro' de lace, W'en de dark is fall - in', W'en de shad - ders creep,

Den dey comes on tip - toe Ter kiss 'im in his sleep

Sweet-est li' l fel - ler, Ev - 'ry-bod - y knows; Dun - no what to call 'im, But he

might - y lak' a rose! Look-in' at his Mam-my Wid eyes so shin - y blue,

Mek' you think that heav'n _____ Is com - in' clost ter you!

MIGHTY LAK A ROSE

1. Sweetest li'l feller,
   Ev'rybody knows;
   Dunno what to call him,
   But he mighty lak a rose!
   Lookin' at his Mammy
   Wid eyes so shiny blue
   Mek you think that heav'n
   Is comin' clost ter you!

2. W'en he's dar a-sleepin',
   In his li'l place,
   Think I see de angels
   Lookin' thro' de lace,
   W'en de dark is fallin',
   W'en de shadows creep,
   Den dey comes on tiptoe
   Ter kiss 'im in his sleep.

3. Sweetest li'l feller,
   Ev'rybody knows;
   Dunno what to call 'im,
   But he mighty lak a rose!
   Lookin' at his Mammy
   Wid eyes so shiny blue,
   Mek you think that heav'n
   Is comin' clost ter you!

An American gem in the then prevalent 'coon' idiom, this also had a tremendous vogue in Britain, where it was a favourite song of the Australian contralto, Ada Crossley.

Frank L. Stanton has been almost lost in the mists; his only other major success as a lyricist appears to have been 'Just a-Wearyin' for You' with music by Carrie Jacobs Bond.

Ethelbert Woodbridge Nevin (1862-1901) came from Pennsylvania and his musical eduaction was a thorough one, for piano, for voice and in composition. His studies took him all over Europe and he taught on both sides of the Atlantic. His compositions included artistic piano pieces — Nevin was considered by his American contemporaries to be the personification of musical refinement — as well as song cycles and individual ballads, one of them, 'The Rosary', being perhaps the most popular 'art-ballad' of all time, and another, 'Little Boy Blue', being the most winsome. He had one other claim to musical immortality: the lilting light orchestral piece, beloved of Palm Court ensembles the world over, 'Narcissus'. The song 'Mighty Lak a Rose' was written in the last year of his life.

Like the simple negro spirituals this song imitates so well, 'Mighty Lak a Rose' will repay a straightforward sincere rendering with just a hint that it is being improvised impromptu.

170

FALMOUTH TOWN

Words by
W.E. Henley

Music by
Harold Fraser-Simson

O, Fal - mouth is a — fine town with — ships — in the bay, ———— And I wish — from my heart it's — there I was to day; ——— I wish from my heart I was far a - way from

It's Home I Want To Be

here, Sit - ting in my par - lour and talk - ing to my dear ____

For it's home, ___ dear - ie, home, — it's

home I want to be. Our top - sails are hoist - ed, and we'll a - way ___ to

sea. O, the oak and the ash and the bon - nie birk - en tree. They're

all ___ grow - ing green in the old coun - trie.

Falmouth Town

It's Home I Want To Be

FALMOUTH TOWN

1. O, Falmouth is a fine town with ships in the bay,
   And I wish from my heart it's there I was today;
   I wish from my heart I was far away from here,
   Sitting in my parlour and talking to my dear.

2. For it's home, dearie, home, it's home I want to be.
   Our topsails are hoisted, and we'll away to sea.
   O, the oak and the ash and the bonnie birken tree,
   They're all growing green in the old countrie.

3. In Baltimore a-walking a lady I did meet
   With her babe on her arm as she came down the street;
   And I thought how I sailed, and the cradle standing ready
   For the pretty little babe that has never seen its daddie.

4. O, if it be a lass, she shall wear a golden ring;
   And if it be a lad, he shall fight for his King:
   With his dirk and his hat and his little jacket blue
   He shall walk the quarter-deck as his daddie used to do.

5. For it's home, dearie, home, it's home I want to be.
   Our topsails are hoisted, and we'll away to sea,
   O, the oak and the ash and the bonnie birken tree,
   They're all growing green in the old countrie.

One of Fraser-Simson's simpler ballads, 'Falmouth Town' still bears the stamp of the composer's exquisite workmanship. The strong, well-made melody is set off by an eminently pianistic accompaniment.

Harold Fraser-Simson (1878-1944) grew up in Sydenham in South London, where the garden of his father's house adjoined the Crystal Palace grounds. His earliest musical experiences were of daily semi-classical concerts given in the Palace. One of five children, he showed an early aptitude for music, but his parents, horrified at the prospect of his becoming a concert pianist, packed him off to France to learn the trade of an importer. He returned to work in the City, but spent every spare moment composing ballads for an eager market. As well as ballads, he began writing musical comedies and it was one of these, *The Maid of the Mountains*, whose phenomenal success allowed him to give up the City and devote himself full-time to composing. A fellow member of the Garrick Club, A.A. Milne, asked Fraser-Simson's advice on setting some of his verses for children in the 'twenties; this led to the sixty seven songs of Christopher Robin, Pooh and their friends which appeared to a rapturous reception. Their final collaboration was on Kenneth Grahame's *The Wind in the Willows* which, as *Toad of Toad Hall*, has never missed a season in the West End since it was written. Fraser-Simson's last years were spent as a country gentleman with his novelist wife, Cicely Devenish, in a castle in Scotland.

There are notes on the poet W.E. Henley on pages 16-17.

Words by
Eugene Field

TODDLES

Music by
A.H. Behrend

The lit-tle toy dog is cov-er'd with dust, But stur-dy and staunch he stands;⸺ And the lit-tle toy sol-dier is red with rust, And his mus-ket moulds in his hands.⸺ Time was when the lit-tle toy dog was new, And the sol-dier was pass-ing fair;

Toddles

That was the time when our Lit-tle Boy Blue Kiss'd them and put them there.

'Now don't you go till I come,' he said, 'And don't you make a-ny noise.' So

tod-dling off to his trun-dle bed, He dreamt of his pret-ty toys; And

as he was dream-ing an An-gel song A-wak-ened our lit-tle Boy Blue. Oh the

177

It's Home I Want To Be

years are ma-ny, the years are long, But the lit-tle toy friends are true.

As faith-ful to Lit-tle Boy Blue they stand,

Each in the same old place, A-wait-ing the touch of a

lit-tle hand, The smile of a lit-tle face. And they

Toddles

won-der while wait-ing the long years through, In the dust of that lit - tle chair, What has be-come of our Lit - tle Boy Blue Since he kiss'd them and put them there, What has be-come of our Lit - tle Boy Blue Since he kiss'd them and put them there.

179

TODDLES

1. The little toy dog is cover'd with dust,
   But sturdy and staunch he stands;
   And the little toy soldier is red with rust,
   And his musket moulds in his hands.
   Time was when the little toy dog was new,
   And the soldier was passing fair;
   That was the time when our Little Boy Blue
   Kiss'd them and put them there.

2. 'Now don't you go till I come,' he said,
   'And don't you make any noise.'
   So toddling off to his trundle bed,
   He dreamt of his pretty toys;
   And as he was dreaming an Angel song
   Awakened our Little Boy Blue.
   Oh the years are many, the years are long,
   But the little toy friends are true.

3. As faithful to Little Boy Blue they stand,
   Each in the same old place,
   Awaiting the touch of a little hand,
   The smile of a little face.
   And they wonder while waiting the long years thro',
   In the dust of that little chair,
   What has become of our Little Boy Blue
   Since he kiss'd them and put them there.

An example of the coy and winning baby songs of the period, 'Toddles' has a well-known verse of American origin (also set by Ethelbert Nevin), its mid-nineteenth-century date evident in the lachrymose extinction of the little hero. Note that he did nothing so crude as to die: no, he was poetically awakened by the song of an angel. The music has a very English feel; when he wrote this Arthur Behrend had already written an archetypal piece in this genre, 'Auntie', with words by Fred E. Weatherly, and a sequel to exploit that success, 'Daddy', which sold a million copies.

Eugene Field (1850-95) is now most remembered for his poems for children, among them this piece and also 'Wynken, Blynken and Nod'. Born in St Louis, Missouri, he was a newspaperman in Chicago, one of the first regular columnists, specializing in humorous snippets and snappy verses, and also a passionate book collector. He is also said to have been that most dispensable of human beings, a practical joker, what was then called a 'prankster', and was thrown out of three colleges for his japes.

One cannot imagine Arthur Henry Behrend (1853-1935) playing practical jokes. His father was a substantial Danzig merchant, and the young Behrend came to England at the age of four to stay at the house of his grandfather, the composer M.W. Balfe who was famous for such imperishable gems as

'Killarney'. A good solid English public school education followed (he was in the Haileybury First XI), and this led to a job in business. However, Behrend decided his talents lay in music, and he commenced an appropriate education at the Royal Academy of Music and in Leipzig. One of his first attempts at song-writing, a setting of Thomas Hood's 'The Song of the Shirt', encouraged *Musical Jottings* to say: 'We don't like it, and therefore leave it to its fate.' Undeterred, he carried on and success soon came with 'Auntie', 'Daddy' and a setting of Tennyson's 'Crossing the Bar' which 'was very appropriate for funerals'. Behrend's published *oeuvre* included two hundred ballads and four cantatas as well as six operas which never saw the printed page.

Behrend's classical musical education must surely be to blame for the curiously incongruous quotation from the sixteenth-century popular tune, 'Sellinger's Round', that makes up the introductory bars to 'Toddles'.

MOTHER O' MINE

Words by
Rudyard Kipling

Music by
S . Liddle

If I were hang'd on the high - est hill, Mo - ther o' Mine, I know whose love would fol - low me still, O Mo - ther o' Mine. If I were

Mother o' Mine

MOTHER O' MINE

1. If I were hang'd on the highest hill,
                    Mother o' Mine,
   I know whose love would follow me still,
                    O Mother o' Mine.

2. If I were drown'd in the deepest sea,
                    Mother o' Mine,
   I know whose tears would come down to me,
                    O Mother o' Mine.

3. If I were damn'd of body and soul,
                    Mother o' Mine,
   I know whose prayers would make me whole,
                    O Mother o' Mine.

For many years Kipling had the popular reputation of being the quintessential patriotic Edwardian, the personification of the imperial theme. The idea was summed up in Max Beerbohm's famous cartoon in which 'Mr Rudyard Kipling takes a bloomin' day aht, on the blasted 'eath, along with Britannia, 'is gurl'. More recently, critical reassessment has shown that the reality was much more complicated: Kipling had become the victim of his own facility with words, and even in his own time the meaning behind his striking prose and poetry did not always reach its mark. This is not the place to mount a discussion of the true Kipling; it is enough merely to point to a few significant facts. His many verses about the soldier of the line, expressed in the colourful language of the barrack-room, have been taken as a glorification of the bellicose. This is a grotesque misreading. True, they had an infectious enthusiasm, but they were startlingly original in suggesting that the hitherto despised common soldiery were actually human beings:

> We aren't no thin red 'eros, nor we aren't no blackguards too,
> But single men in barricks, most remarkable like you;
> An' if sometimes our conduck isn't all your fancy paints,
> Why, single men in barricks don't grow into plaster saints.

Kipling saw through the divisiveness of class ('The colonel's lady and Judy O'Grady are sisters under the skin'), the stultifying aspects of a public school education ('the flannelled fools at the wicket or the muddied oafs at the goals'), the suspect imperialism of the politician (remember the 'Jelly-bellied Flag-flapper' in *Stalky & Co.*), and the cheap patriotism of the popular press:

> If England was what England seems,
>   An' not the England of our dreams,
> But only putty, brass, an' paint
>   'Ow quick we'd drop her! But she ain't!

184

In fact, Kipling's dream of England was a fierce and proud one, honest and responsible in the best Victorian tradition. For all his distaste for cant and hypocrisy he was essentially a man of his time, and the sentiment behind the poem 'Mother o' Mine' is utterly in accord with dozens of other filial encomiums. It is typical of the poet, however, that even here the sugar is balanced by a sharper flavour: serious reference to hanging and damning was hardly normal currency in the drawing-room.

The life-story of Rudyard Kipling (1865-1936) is sufficiently well known not to require summary here, but it is interesting to see how his reputation is changing; at one time it was his short stories, particularly those in the Indian setting that he knew so intimately, that appeared to guarantee immortality whilst there were mixed feelings about his poetry. The pendulum has swung, and it is now generally recognized that he was, however flawed, one of Britain's major poets. Many of his verses were set to music by various hands and a surprisingly large number live on in performance: 'The Road to Mandalay' in the famous setting by Oley Speaks (there were others), 'Boots', 'The Smuggler's Song' and 'Rolling Down to Rio'.

Samuel Liddle (c. 1868-?) was born in Leeds and educated at the Royal College of Music. Best known as an accompanist, he was also a solo pianist and a busy composer of ballads. They included 'Christmas Bells' and that singular piece of religiosity 'Abide with Me', written for Dame Clara Butt whom he accompanied. She also popularized another of his items, 'A Song of Good Courage'.

Liddle's setting of this ballad is economic but subtle. Notice how he increases the intensity of the words 'Mother o' Mine' in each verse by raising the final note of the phrase every time it appears.

STONECRACKER JOHN

Words by
Fred E. Weatherly

Music by
Eric Coates

Stonecracker John

187

It's Home I Want To Be

green-er - y, Oh whack fol the rid-dle oh, I chuck-le and say, I'd

crack 'em, and whack em, if I had my way. So I would, now, Yes I

would, now, If I had my way!

When the sweet - hearts go by an' the girls look so

cud-dle-some, What _ makes all the young men so moo-dy and mud-dle-some? Oh

Stonecracker John

whack fol the rid - dle oh, if I had my way, I'd take 'em, an' shake 'em, an' show 'em what to say. So I would, now, Yes I would, now, I'd show 'em the way!

But I mayn't live much long - er to con - tin - ue my his - to - ry, An'

It's Home I Want To Be

what's to be-come of me, well, that is a mys-ter-y, So whack fol the rid-dle oh! like the stones I do say, You may crack me, an' whack me, but I've had my day. So I have, then, Yes I have, then, Yes,— I've had my day! Oh whack fol the rid-dle oh, oh rid-dle oh. crack me, and you may crack me, an' whack me, but I've had my day!

STONECRACKER JOHN

1. I sits by the roadside with great regularity,
   And I cracks up the stones for the Highway Authority,
   Oh whack fol the riddle oh, I earns all my pay,
   For I cracks 'em an' whacks 'em for ninepence a day.
   So I do, now,
   Yes I do, now,
   All for ninepence a day!

2. When the grand folks go by on their wild-cat machinery,
   They kicks up a dust an' they spoils all the greenery,
   Oh whack fol the riddle oh, I chuckle and say,
   I'd crack 'em an' whack 'em, if I had my way.
   So I would, now,
   Yes I would, now,
   If I had my way!

3. When the sweethearts go by an' the girls look so cuddlesome,
   What makes all the young men so moody and muddlesome?
   Oh whack fol the riddle oh, if I had my way,
   I'd take 'em and shake 'em, and show 'em what to say.
   So I would, now,
   Yes I would, now,
   I'd show 'em the way!

4. But I mayn't live much longer to continue my history,
   An' what's to become o' me, that is a mystery,
   So whack fol the riddle oh, like the stones I do say,
   You may crack me, an' whack me, but I've had my day.
   So I have, then,
   Yes I have, then,
   Yes, I've had my day!

'I have written several rustic songs,' wrote Fred E. Weatherly, 'humbly endeavouring to copy the old humorous songs . . . the music of which exactly reproduces the style and spirit of the old English folk-songs.' He possessed, he claimed, 'intimate knowledge of rustic folk', and recorded that the homely philosophy of his family's gardener and general factotum, Robbins, was inspiration for 'Stonecracker John'. He even claimed that if it had been not for the reference to motor cars and the label of his name critics would not have detected the modern origin of the song. That breathtaking statement shows clearly the extent to which the real and the spurious in folk-music could still confuse the Edwardians. There is more information on Weatherly on pages 113-14.

One of this century's favourite composers of light orchestral material, Eric Coates (1886-1958) came from Nottinghamshire and made his mark early. He won a scholarship to the Royal Academy of Music in 1906 and even as a student he was attracting attention for his ballads, his settings of Shakespeare songs being produced by Mrs Henry Wood at the Promenade Concerts. For some years he was principal viola at Queen's Hall. He wrote quantities of tuneful marches, orchestral suites, overtures and incidental music for stage and film, and also chamber music; although strictly light-weight, his output has sparkle, melody and charm which, given its innate musicality, still delights.

Amy Woodforde-Finden

Arthur Behrend

William Boosey

Frances Allitsen

Three composers and a publisher

BEYOND THE DAWN

Words by
Fred E. Weatherly

Music by
Wilfrid Sanderson

What of the day, O wea-ry eyes? The day is hard and long; The wind a-cross the fair-est skies, It hath a drea-ry song.___ O wea-ry eyes, be com-fort-ed, The dear God know-eth

Beyond the Dawn

best, ____ How - ev - er long the __ day may be, The night shall _ give us rest. ____

What of the night, O ach - ing hearts? The night may bring you pain, Your dear - est dreams may mock at you, Your prayers may seem in vain. ____ O ach - ing hearts, be sat - is - fied, Look

It's Home I Want To Be

up and have no fear, _____ The sad - dest night, the ___ dark - est tide, The dawn will __ soon be here.

What of the night, the long, long night, The pass - ing bells that call, _____ The Val - ley of the Sha - dow, And the grass that cov - ers

Beyond the Dawn

BEYOND THE DAWN

1.   What of the day, O weary eyes?
    The day is hard and long;
    The wind across the fairest skies,
    It hath a dreary song.
    O weary eyes, be comforted,
    The dear God knoweth best,
    However long the day may be,
    The night shall give us rest.

2.   What of the night, O aching hearts?
    The night may bring you pain;
    Your dearest dreams may mock at you,
    Yours prayers may seem in vain.
    O aching hearts, be satisfied,
    Look up and have no fear,
    The saddest night, the darkest tide,
    The dawn will soon be here.

3.   What of the night, the long, long night,
    The passing bells that call,
    The Valley of the Shadow,
    And the grass that covers all?
    Be not afraid, God's arm is nigh,
    To guide you through the gloom,
    The morning of Eternity
    Begins beyond the tomb!

This is the first of the songs that Fred E. Weatherly wrote with Wilfrid Sanderson; there are two others in this collection. It is an utterly Edwardian ballad. The verses are misty and portentous — and bland, the sentiment blindingly obvious and the vocabulary drawn from the well-used store of 'night', 'dawn', 'wind', 'tide', 'song', 'dreams', 'aching hearts' and similar poetic impedimenta. God is introduced to give the whole thing solemnity, as is, with fine inevitability in the last line, the tomb. Notes on the talented poet and composer are on pages 113-14 and 61-2.

What may appear rather unpromising on the page is, in fact, highly effective in performance. Sanderson's setting transcends the ponderous verse and builds to a massive climax. It is worth noting the echoing bells and the descent into the Valley of the Shadow in the final verse. Pianists will particularly relish the sonorous falling bass which acts as a springboard for the rising melody in the treble.

FRIEND O' MINE

Words by
Fred E. Weatherly

Music by
Wilfrid Sanderson

It's Home I Want To Be

do, _____ The gold you've struck, the fame you've won,

And let me joy — with you!

When you are sad and heart a - cold, And all your skies are

dark, Tell me the dreams that mock'd your hold,

The shafts that miss'd the mark. Am I not yours for

200

Friend o' Mine

weal or woe? How else can friends prove true?

molto rit.

Tell me what breaks and brings you low, And let me stand — with you!

colla voce   *sf*   *ten.*

allargando   *sf*   *molto rit.*   *p* LENTO   So when the night falls

LENTO   *ppp*   *trem.*

trem - u - lous, When the last lamp burns low, _____ And

solem   *rit.*

one of us or both of us The long, lone road must

legato rit.

It's Home I Want To Be

FRIEND O' MINE

1. When you are happy, friend o' mine,
    And all your skies are blue,
    Tell me your luck, your fortune fine,
    And let me laugh with you.
    Tell me the hopes that spur you on,
    The deeds you mean to do,
    The gold you've struck, the fame you've won,
    And let me joy - with you!

2. When you are sad and heart a-cold,
    And all your skies are dark,
    Tell me the dreams that mock'd your hold,
    The shafts that miss'd the mark.
    Am I not yours for weal or woe?
    How else can friends prove true?
    Tell me what breaks and brings you low,
    And let me stand - with you!

3. So, when the night falls tremulous,
    When the last lamp burns low,
    And one of us or both of us
    The long, lone road must go,
    Look with your dear old eyes in mine,
    Give me a handshake true;
    Whatever fate our souls await
    Let me be there - with you!

'Friend o' Mine' was written by Fred E. Weatherly in 1912, an extremely busy year for him, both in the production of songs and in the heaviest volume of legal work he had ever had as a barrister. The tenor Michael Maybrick, now better known as a composer under the name of Stephen Adams, was a close friend of Weatherly, who described him as businesslike and decisive, always letting the lyricist know at once which verses of his he would like to set. The text of 'Friend o' Mine' was despatched to Maybrick as 'a real heart to heart talk' between writer and composer, but the latter failed to acknowledge its receipt, the first time he had been silent when offered a song by Weatherly. When Maybrick visited the poet in Bath in July 1913 he was obviously ill, and never referred to the piece which had been written for him as a tribute to their deep friendship. Within a few weeks Maybrick was dead, and afterwards Weatherly liked to think that the song had touched its recipient so deeply that he could neither set it to music nor speak of it. Other explanations occur to the observer: perhaps the composer's reaction to the quality of the verse was such that he thought it kinder never to refer to it; perhaps as an elderly man he found the touch of *memento mori* slightly offensive; or perhaps the offering simply went astray in the mails. Ever practical, Weatherly submitted his lyric to another friend, Wilfrid Sanderson, who duly set it; they dedicated it to Maybrick.

There are short biographies of Weatherly and Sanderson on pages 113-14 and 61-2.

Very much in the style of the previous song, Sanderson's accompaniment is restrained and, at the same time, complementary to the vocal line. In the hands of a sensitive accompanist and singer, 'Friend o' Mine' still has the power to charm today.

5

Two's Company

Three Songs for Two Voices

DOWN THE VALE

Words by
Gunby Hadath

Music by
Frank L. Moir

Down the Vale

wel - come and there's rap - ture, o'er moor - land and o'er dale; But

wel - come and there's rap - ture, o'er moor - land and o'er dale; But none, but

none so glad as I am, lad, lass, when you come down the vale.

none so glad as I am lass, lad, when you come down the vale.

Stars up a - bove, find ye my love, Tell him her the night is fair;

Stars up a - bove, Tell her him tell her him the night is fair, tell her, him,

Peep from the skies in - to $\begin{smallmatrix}his\\her\end{smallmatrix}$ eyes, Leav-ing my im-age there.

Peep from the skies, Leav - ing, leav-ing my im - age there.

Where vale and cop -pice meet, $\begin{smallmatrix}lad,\\lass,\end{smallmatrix}$ my tryst for thee I

Where vale and cop -pice meet,— $\begin{smallmatrix}lass,\\lad,\end{smallmatrix}$ my tryst for thee I

keep, The hare - bells at my feet, $\begin{smallmatrix}lad,\\lass,\end{smallmatrix}$ are smil-ing in their sleep; And

keep, The hare - bells at my feet, $\begin{smallmatrix}lass,\\lad,\end{smallmatrix}$ are smil-ing in their sleep; And

Down the Vale

Two's Company

Leav - ing my im - age there. When we go down the vale, lad, lass, the

leav - ing my im - age there.

last long Vale of Tears No ter - ror shall pre - vail, lad, lass, and there shall be no

Tempo I

fears; For though the sha - dows dark - en and ev - 'ry star be pale, I

Tempo I

For though the sha - dows dark - en and ev - 'ry star be pale, I shall, I

Down the Vale

shall not fear_ if you_ are near_ When we go down the Vale. An - gels a - bove_
_ shall sing our love In a di-vine re - frain, Where Love a - lone
hom - age doth own, Where love a - lone doth reign._____

shall not fear if you are near When we go down the Vale. An - gels a -
bove In a di - vine a di - vine re - frain; Where Love a -
lone, a - lone doth reign Where love a - lone doth reign._____

DOWN THE VALE

1. When you come down the vale, lad, there's singing in the trees,
   There's music in the gale, lad, and music in the breeze,
   There's welcome and there's rapture, o'er moorland and o'er dale;
   But none so glad as I am, lad, when you come down the vale.

   > Stars up above, find ye my love,
   > Tell him the night is fair;
   > Peep from the skies into his eyes,
   > Leaving my image there.

2. Where vale and coppice meet, lad, my tryst for thee I keep,
   The harebells at my feet, lad, are smiling in their sleep;
   And every bonny birdie, lad, wings home his mate to greet,
   And croons to me of love and thee, where vale and coppice meet.

   > Stars up above, find ye my love,
   > Tell him the night is fair;
   > Peep from the skies into his eyes,
   > Leaving my image there.

3. When we go down the vale, lad, the last, long Vale of Tears,
   No terror shall prevail, lad, and there shall be no fears;
   For though the shadows darken and ev'ry star be pale,
   I shall not fear if you are near when we go down the Vale.

   > Angels above shall sing our love
   > In a divine refrain;
   > Where Love alone homage doth own,
   > Where Love alone doth reign!

Despite an *oeuvre* of several hundred published songs, Gunby Hadath is totally forgotten. He was educated at Cambridge University and achieved some standing as a lyricist, a librettist of musical sketches, an adapter of musical plays from the French and a writer of boys' stories. Much of his life was spent in France where he was sufficiently well considered to be created a Citoyen d'honneur of St-Gervais-les-bains.

Now equally obscure, Frank Lewis Moir (1852-1904) was as prolific a composer as Hadath was a poet. The titles of his immense output, which were completely characteristic of contemporary taste, 'Ah Me', 'A Knight of Old', 'Grieve Not Dear Heart' and so on, strike no chord in memory now, and only 'Down the Vale' retains the shreds of celebrity. Towards the end of his life, Moir was active in the agitation in the musical world to overcome the inadequacies of copyright legislation that enabled pirates to reprint sheet music with virtual impunity.

Moir's charming setting of Hadath's poem repays a full-blooded performance. Singers should beware of wallowing in the purple harmonies as a fairly sprightly tempo is infinitely more telling.

Sir Edward Elgar

Sir Charles Villiers Stanford

Sir Frederic Cowen

Sir Hubert Parry

Four 'Establishment' composers

GOOD NIGHT, DEAR HEART

Words by
Harold Simpson

Music by
Ernest Newton

Good Night, Dear Heart

Two's Company

I'll dream of ___ thee, I'll dream of thee till morn-ing breaks a - gain.

When in the gen-tle arms of sleep I lie.

When in the gen-tle arms of sleep you lie,

Thy love shall guard and watch o'er me:

My love shall guard and watch o'er thee:

No shade of grief or sor-row shall come

Good Night, Dear Heart

Two's Company

Good Night, Dear Heart

GOOD NIGHT, DEAR HEART

1.   Good night, dear heart!
    Stars in the sky are gleaming:
    Dear heart, good night!
    Calm be thy hours of dreaming:
    Ah! my beloved! Ah! my beloved!
    God keep thee safe till morning breaks again.

2.   Good night, dear heart!
    Absence but brings thee nearer,
    Dear heart, good night!
    Parting but makes thee dearer:
    Ah! my beloved, Ah! my beloved!
    I'll dream of thee till morning breaks again.

3.   When in the gentle arms of sleep you lie,
    My love shall guard and watch o'er thee:
    No shade of grief or sorrow shall come nigh.
    Then on the wings of love shall fancy fly
    To charm my dreams with thoughts of thee,
    For thou art mine, beloved, till I die.

4.   Good night, dear heart!
    Part we, but not with grieving,
    Dear heart, good night!
    Brief is the hour of leaving:
    Ah! my beloved! Ah! my beloved!
    God keep thee mine till morning breaks again.

The writer of verses for many successful ballads, Harold Simpson received an accolade from his fellow lyricist Fred E. Weatherly who considered his productions of literary value. Unfortunately, 'Good Night, Dear Heart' provides little evidence for that judgment. His work included song cycles for the young Landon Ronald, including one favourite of Nellie Melba's, 'Down in the Forest'. Simpson was the author, too, of a history of drawing-room songs, *A Century of Ballads, 1810-1910*, which is a fascinating source of information about the whole phenomenon.

Although now an obscure figure, Ernest Newton composed several immensely popular ballads. Born in Llandudno, he was the son of a parson, went to Cambridge and had a sound musical education. His style of composition ranged from the bounciness of 'The Beat of the Drum' and 'The Drum Major' (which had words by Fred E. Weatherly) to the tenderness of 'For Love of You' and 'Roses by Summer Forsaken', which were in the repertoire of Dame Clara Butt. He could evidently turn his hand to any musical requirement: his various jobs included director of the London School of Accompaniment, church organist and song editor for the publisher Novello.

His setting for 'Good Night, Dear Heart' is extremely telling in performance and offers great scope to 'committed' performers.

THE MAIDEN IN GREY

Words by
G. Hubi-Newcombe

Music by
Reginald S. Barnicott

The sun-beams are hot, and your bon-net will fade,

Won't you walk in the shad-ows with me, pret-ty maid?

I thank you, sir, no, I'm, not go-ing your way,_____ I must haste to the mar-ket, so

leave me, I pray, so leave me, I pray.

The rain-drops are fall-ing, are fall-ing on you,_____ Come be-

The Maiden in Grey

Two's Company

I thank you, sir, tearful, I know,— And my heart it is long-ing to comfort you, so.

no, mother'll scold if I stay,— And what - ev - er she tells me, of *course* I o - bey!

Fa la

yes, of *course* I o - bey!

la la la la, yes, of *course* you o - bey!

O, just whis-per you

love me, you love me, I know, _____ For your pret-ty shy eyes, _____ they are

If my eyes, sir, are speak-ing, there's nought I need say, _____

tell - ing me so. _____

_ But if moth-er says 'yes' well per-haps, then, I may. O just whis-per you love me, you

O just whis-per you love me, you

Two's Company

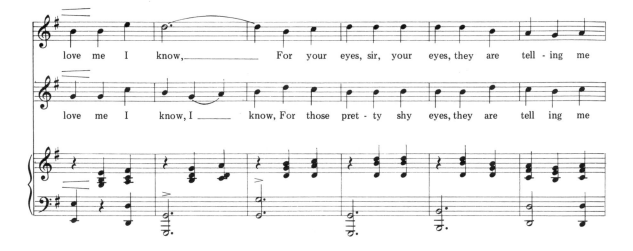

love me I know,_____ For your eyes, sir, your eyes, they are tell - ing me

love me I know, I _____ know, For those pret - ty shy eyes, they are tell ing me

so. Fa la la la la la, you __ love me I know. Fa la la la la la

so Fa la la la la, you __ love me I know, Fa la la la la

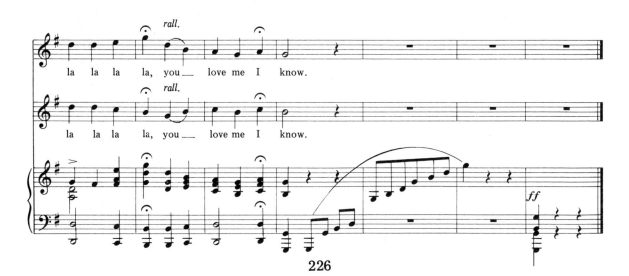

la la la la, you __ love me I know.

la la la la, you __ love me I know.

THE MAIDEN IN GREY

The sunbeams are hot and your bonnet will fade,
Won't you walk in the shadows with me, pretty maid?

I thank you, sir, no, I'm not going your way,
I must haste to the market, so leave me, I pray.

The raindrops are falling, are falling on you,
Come beneath my umbrella, there's just room for two.

I thank you, sir, no, I must hurry away,
But I think that perhaps - I might - some other day.
Fa la la la la la, perhaps some other day.

Sweet maid, you are sighing, you're tearful, I know,
And my heart it is longing to comfort you, so.

I thank you, sir, no, mother'll scold if I stay,
And whatever she tells me, of *course* I obey!
Fa la la la la la, yes, of *course* I obey!

O, just whisper you love me, you love me I know,
For your pretty shy eyes, they are telling me so.

If my eyes, sir, are speaking, there's nought I need say,
But if mother says 'yes', well perhaps then, I may.

O, just whisper you love me, you love me I know,
For you pretty shy eyes, they are telling me so.
Fa la la la la la, you love me I know.

If ever there was the equivalent of the delicate art of Kate Greenaway in ballad form, this is it, and it is not surprising that the verses come from the genteel pen of Madame G. Hubi-Newcombe. She wrote lyrics for sundry composers including Henri Pontet (actually Piccolomini), Henri Trotère, with whom she produced 'Within Your Heart' which two publishers turned down, believing it to be a childish joke, and also Edward St Quentin, their collaboration resulting in 'A Voice from Heaven', an excessively coy piece about a child and an angel. She also provided words for a couple of operettas and a prize hymn. Later in life she offered instruction in voice production, singing, composition and the organ. This formidable lady lived in Purley.

The editors of this volume have so far failed to find any traces of the composer Reginald S. Barnicott; this song evidently represents his sole claim on immortality.

Firmly rooted in the 'Oh, no, John, no' tradition of rustic romances, 'The Maiden in Grey' demands a 'visual' performance that points the words and music effectively. Given this, the song comes very convincingly to life and has power to charm even in an age when courtship is less protracted and considerably less formal than it used to be.

Sir Charles Santley

Edward Lloyd

Plunket Greene

Ben Davies

Four lions of the ballad concert

Index

TITLES

The page numbers in **bold** *type refer to the beginning of a song.*

FIRST LINES

POETS, COMPOSERS, SINGERS, MUSICIANS, PUBLISHERS, ETC.

The page numbers in **bold** *type refer to brief biographies; those in* italics *refer to illustrations.*